To Elizabeth Hollingworth

With best wishes

Camilla Denning

Notes from the Canary Islands

by

Camille Lenning

DORRANCE PUBLISHING CO., INC.
PITTSBURGH, PENNSYLVANIA 15222

ISBN # 0-8059-3906-7
Printed in the United States of America

First Printing

For information or to order additional books, please write:
Dorrance Publishing Co., Inc.
643 Smithfield Street
Pittsburgh, Pennsylvania 15222
U.S.A.

Contents

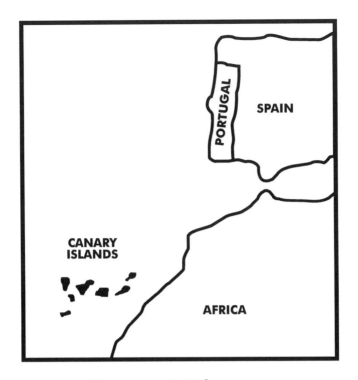

Voyage of Discovery

The Canary Islands, seventy miles off the west coast of Africa and almost a thousand miles south of the Iberian Peninsula, are, nevertheless, a province of Spain and have been since before the time of Christopher Columbus. In fact, this was his point of departure for the New World. In addition to taking on provisions, it has been said that he was also taking the opportunity to visit a noblewoman who had been exiled to the Islands by Queen Isabela because the king was in love with her—or vice versa—or both. Whatever the reasons for his stopover, Columbus placed the Canaries squarely and irrevocably on the historical map. I am reminded of the first leg of his journey as we speed south from Madrid—a mere two and one half hours by air compared to his several days by Caravel.

In a way, I also am on a voyage of discovery, hoping to find out if the islands really are the ideal place for winter vacations and eventual retirement. I am headed for Gran Canaria, one of the largest of the group of seven that make up the archipelago.

As we approach the airport I watch eagerly for a first glimpse of land. When it comes into view, it is arid and volcanic with brown, rock-strewn plains merging in the distance into foothills and jagged peaks. Not too inviting, I have to admit. On the other hand, when looking for a place to enjoy the sun, I have learned that "arid" is a word to be respected. The highway to the city passes through a succession of industrial areas with clusters of concrete block housing and stands of dusty cactus beside the road. Here and there fields of tomatoes are covered with vast areas of plastic—practical but hardly picturesque.

Then, finally, we round a bend and there, lying in a huge curve before a backdrop of steep hills, is Las Palmas, its center mostly white and high rise but splashed with color at the outskirts where blocks of old, brightly-painted houses have withstood the ravages of urban renewal.

On the other side of the highway, huge waves explode against a formidable breakwater and clouds of dazzling white foam fall back onto clearest aqua. It looks immaculate and refreshing, and my spirits rise at the sight of it. We pass the familiar Lions Club logo but with a difference—this one says "Club de Leones y de Leonas" (Club of Lions and Lionesses)—also refreshing.

On now to the beach area where I have a reservation at a sea-front hotel, except that, being one person, I am relegated to a room at the side with an uninterrupted view of an apartment building across the street. A woman over there reclines comfortably on her terrace, gazing contentedly at what I assume to be the ocean. It occurs to me that if I do decide to buy something in Las Palmas, that which she is enjoying might suit me very nicely. Little do I know that after a long search and a number of false starts, fate will lead me to that very building and, although I couldn't swear to it, maybe to that very same apartment.

On my first day, a real estate agent riffles through his card file and produces an apartment with precisely the characteristics I have in mind. I am overjoyed! Unfortunately, the owner has gone off on an extended vacation with the only set of keys in existence—the first of many disappointments. However, I am confident that somewhere in this labyrinth of narrow streets, the perfect apartment is waiting to be discovered and, over the next week, I become increasingly determined to track it down.

When it appears, it is not exactly perfect, but of all the places I have seen it is the only one giving onto the beach. I meet the owner—a sad-faced gentleman accompanied by his small son.

"It is for him I am selling, Señora. Since he was born he has been in poor health. It has cost me everything," he explains.

Actually, the child looks perfectly healthy—robust in fact. But, from what I have seen, the price is about what it should be so I make no attempt to bargain—a serious tactical error, I soon discover.

With all in readiness for the contract, the thought of owning my own place is unexpectedly exhilarating and, in the privacy of my hotel room, I execute a few gleeful dance steps to the accompaniment of a subdued rebel yell.

My lawyer announces that he will be unable to attend the signing, but designates a colleague who, he assures me, is also an experienced lawyer. Not that it really matters, because he is not going to show up either. However, my agent collects me and we speed off to our appointment in high spirits.

The seller is waiting in the ante-chamber. My agent scans the contract. Suddenly there is a bellow of rage as he leaps to his feet and directs a tirade of abuse at the owner. When he smashes his fist into the table, I feel it is time to find out what's going on.

"Basta, señores! Enough, gentlemen!" I say in my best Spanish. "What seems to be the difficulty?" The "difficulty," I discover, is the matter of roughly ten thousand dollars, U.S.—the amount by which the seller has upped the price. In fact, the contract I have come to sign already includes the revised figure.

After a few thrusts and parries, we sweep out with what I hope is a great show of disdain and cool indifference. Underneath, I am terribly disappointed and also mad as hell. Furthermore, I was planning to return to New York the following day, a fact known, incidentally, to the seller and perhaps not unconnected with his decision to boost the price at the last moment.

Downhearted and somewhat dazed by this sudden turn of events, I make my way almost mechanically to a favorite beach-front restaurant where a sympathetic waiter has been following my progress during the search. I tell him my troubles and we agree that a double vodka might help.

It is too early for the dinner crowd, but one of the local fishermen is at the bar accompanied by his dog, and beside me a group of his companions are engaged in animated conversation—not so distracted, however, that they forget to be hospitable. One offers me a cigarette, which I have to decline since I've kicked the habit. Another gallantly proffers a small fried fish from their communal platter, extending it delicately by the tail between a huge thumb and forefinger. He is a little drunk, but kindly, and I accept the offer with what I hope are appropriate thanks.

Meanwhile, my waiter has stopped by solicitously and promises that in a few minutes there will be some typical music of the Canaries. What with the vodka and the fish and one thing and another, I am beginning to feel quite cheerful. The instrumentalists emerge playing "It's Three O'clock in the Morning," but that's all right too—maybe it was filched from them in the first place.

In any case, my disposition is greatly improved and the following day, I have decided to postpone my departure for another week and return to the fray. As I stroll along the sea front, I gaze speculatively at an apartment building—"Casa Manuel" it is called—the one next to my hotel with the woman ensconced on the terrace. I had admired it when I first arrived but I was timid then. Now, with a week of experience behind me, I enter boldly and ask whether any of the apartments are for sale. The reply is non-committal. It is suggested that I come back and see the owner, Don Manuel, at five o'clock in the afternoon—a fateful hour, I note warily—the traditional time for the bull fights to begin.

When I return for my appointment, I am led by a young woman into the first-floor restaurant. She gestures toward a table occupied by two men. "That is Don Manuel," she says, indicating the one facing me. "He will be through in a few minutes," and she pulls out a chair for me at a nearby table.

Don Manuel is fortyish, slim but wiry, proudly erect, and dressed entirely in black. Apart from a courteous inclination of the head from time to time, he says nothing. His companion, on the other hand, never stops talking. I wonder if he is a potential buyer. When the Don finally speaks, all doubt is eliminated.

"I never reduce my price," he says quietly but firmly. Is it my imagination or was the statement somehow projected in my direction? The visitor leaves, crestfallen.

Don Manuel approaches my table and introduces himself. I state the purpose of my visit and accept his invitation to join him in a cup of coffee.

There is one apartment available. If I would care to see it, he would be glad to show it to me. He leads the way. It faces south, has a good view of the ocean, one bedroom, a terrace, and it is completely furnished and equipped. Intuition nods vigorously, but the price is more than I intended to pay.

He ushers me back into the elevator, but when the door opens and I step out, I am not on the first floor as I had expected, but in the foyer of the penthouse.

"Come," he says proudly, "I will show you my apartment." I enter, expecting the lady of the house to appear, but the decor is pure bachelor—heavy, leather upholstered furniture, a handsome semi-circular bar—and no knickknacks. Glass doors open onto an enormous terrace with magnificent views of the Atlantic on one side and the port and city of Las Palmas on the other.

"Now this is the apartment I should like to have!" I exclaim enthusiastically.

"My house is your house, Señora," he responds with a courtly bow. In Spain, these words are widely used as a general expression of hospitality, but, is there just a hint of possible fringe benefits should I decide to buy the apartment downstairs? I arrange to meet him the following day with a final decision.

That night, exhausted from a week of apartment hunting with its hopes and frustrations and now, faced with a difficult decision, I eventually fall into a troubled sleep. Not long afterwards—about a minute and a half it seems—I become aware of music—something resembling the massed bands of the armed forces. They are next door and sleep is impossible. I calculate how much I would need for the down-payment on the apartment I had looked at this afternoon. It is perfect for me, but if the seller insists on cash, the deal is definitely off—and I will be devastated. Payment over three years, usually the maximum, would be tight. Two years, hazardous. One year, improbable.

The band is still going strong. Back to the financial situation. Perhaps if I were to do my own cleaning for a year? The idea is too depressing and I cast it aside. I doze once more and seem to have slept during what was left of the night.

I wake with a blinding headache—as hungover, I reflect bitterly, as though I had been invited to their rotten party. Later, I pull myself together, dress as carefully as I can for my meeting about the apartment, and survey the result in the mirror. Pretty awful, I have to admit—and just when I wanted to look my best.

As before, my appointment is in the restaurant—and at the same fateful hour. When I arrive the Don has not yet appeared. When he does I am shocked. *He* looks worse that *I* do! And, in addition, he has a black eye! Instinctively, I know I should disregard his appearance, so I am alarmed to hear myself asking flatly:

"What happened to your face?"

"An accident with my car," he responds stiffly.

"How terrible! I'm sorry." On closer inspection, I realize that, in addition to the eye, he is actually quite banged up. "How did it happen?" I ask with genuine concern.

"In fact," he replies, in an abrupt reversal, "I did not have an accident, but a problem with the police." Now he is describing the stupidity, ineffectiveness, and gross negligence of his lawyer and this, together with one or two other details, leads me to the irrefutable conclusion that he had spent last night in the pokey. I am bowled over!

He puts a hand to his forehead and closes his eyes for a second. *Perhaps,* I think, *I should go away and leave him in peace.* Then, like a flash, it dawns on me! This is no time to retreat. This is the moment of *truth!* My adversary has been delivered to me appropriately bloodied and battered, if not by the picadors, then just as effectively by the local constabulary. All that remains is for me to move in for the kill. There is a fleeting moment of compunction—firmly suppressed as I recall the circumstances surrounding the apartment I lost.

He is still going on about the events of the night before. I size up the situation and prepare to maneuver myself into a favorable position.

"I find it inconceivable," I say indignantly, "that a gentleman in your position should be treated in this way. Is there no recourse?"

"Perhaps if I had a lawyer who is not an incompetent idiot," he replies throwing up his hands in despair.

"I can well imagine how you feel," I respond. "One pays these people such enormous fees and it is in just such a crisis that one expects their assistance." He looks somewhat gratified at my depth of understanding.

"Perhaps," I say tentatively, my fingers crossed under the table, "you would prefer not to discuss the apartment today."

"Not at all. Not at all, Señora. Tell me what you have decided," he replies.

"Well," I assure him, being careful not to go overboard, "it is a nice apartment. More or less what I am looking for. I can see that the building is managed efficiently and well maintained." A wan smile appears.

"However," I add, "the price is more than I intended to pay." The smile vanishes.

"I wonder," I continue, "if it would be *convenient* to include the furniture and equipment in the price?"

"Convenient?" he says, confused.

"Well, in these days of tight money, I realize that even if one would *like* to give in a little it is not always possible." He looks at me scornfully.

"To me the price of the furniture is of no consequence. Include it if you wish." So far, so good. He is holding his head now, probably wishing I would hurry up and get it over.

"Then it is agreed?" he asks, without looking up.

"Well, except for the period of payment," I add hastily.

"Take as long as you like, Señora," he moans, obviously hoping to put an end to the whole miserable business and go back to bed. "A life-time, if you wish."

"In that case," I say, extending a hand, "it's a deal."

"I am very happy that you have decided to join us," he says, making an effort to be congenial. "I will have the contract prepared at once."

"Wonderful. And for the period of payment, I think five years would be quite suitable," I say craftily.

"*Five* years?" he repeats incredulously, snapping upright.

"You said a lifetime if I wish," I reply, injured.

"Yes, but that was just a...a...remark," he stammers.

"But five years is less than a lifetime—I hope," I wheedle.

"I have never agreed to more than two years and, as I am sure you are aware, three years is the absolute maximum that anybody allows," he blusters.

"Very well," I say, shrugging helplessly. "Since we shook hands on the deal, I wouldn't think of backing out, so if you intend to break your wor.... I mean if you wish to change your mind, I suppose I must accept it."

"Señora," he says, leaning across the table and narrowing his eyes, "I have never cheated anybody in my life. Evidently you feel I made a commitment when I said a lifetime. Very well then. Let us establish your age, determine your life expectancy and have done with it."

"No. No." I protest. "I do not wish to be unreasonable. Five years is quite adequate."

"Adequate," he echoes in apparent disbelief. Then with quiet resignation, "Very well," and on that note the interview ends.

As I leave, Don Manuel remains seated, staring thoughtfully into space. He glances down and a flicker of pain crosses his face—as though he has just noticed a little blood on the sand and realized that it is his. And are those cries of "Ole" I hear in the distance?

I make a carefully restrained exit, somehow resisting an almost overwhelming desire to skip the last few steps. Afterwards, when I have calmed down, I wonder whether I really did do that well. Perhaps the Don was in fact, the real winner. However, at the closing a few days later, although evidently recovered from his brush with the police, he is not only terse but positively glum, which I find vastly reassuring.

"Thank God, it's over," I murmur with a sigh of relief, and as the plane lifts off and heads for New York, I settle back, happily clutching my handbag with the precious contract. Actually, I reflect, as I gently rotate the ice cubes in my drink, it really wasn't *that* difficult and, as I savor the delights of ownership and the cocktail wagon appears for the second time, the problems I had encountered are forgotten in the sheer, undreamed-of rapture of owning my very own place. A place to which I will return intermittently and with increasing frequency over the next twenty years.

So, Columbus did *his* thing and now I have done mine.

A State of Mourning?

After a year I am back in Las Palmas to stay for the first time in my newly-acquired apartment, and I am nervous about it. Will it really be as perfect as it appeared during my brief inspection? I am reassured almost at once. I feel comfortable in it from the first moment. At night the gentle rhythm of the surf lulls me to sleep, and the sun wakes me in the morning. Could anything be more pleasant?

Don Manuel checks to make sure I have everything I need. He appears each day around five in the afternoon to spend time in his restaurants. First, the smorgasbord on the first floor where the Swedes and other Europeans stream in for dinner around six or seven; then the more formal steak house on the second floor, which doesn't begin to serve until nine; and after that he is off to his nightclub. He continues to dress in unrelieved black and it occurs to me that he might be in mourning.

This impression is reinforced when I go to the steak house for dinner one evening and he is there with a pretty little girl of about eight, whom he introduces as his daughter. She is nicely dressed except for a pair of new high-heeled shoes completely unsuitable for a child of her age, which she is intent upon showing off. I imagine that Manuel may have taken her shopping and these were what she insisted on.

"I have the most wonderful daughter in the whole world," he exclaims, hugging and kissing her. She smiles briefly, but her expression is sad and she accepts his attention passively. I feel sorry for her and wonder if her mother might have died. This would explain why Manuel is in mourning and why he lives alone in his penthouse apartment.

A few days later, my sixteen-year-old goddaughter arrives to spend a week with me. Tall, blond, and beautiful, she attracts a great deal of admiration and, as a sort of spin off, I find myself receiving more than my usual quota of attention. Manuel immediately invites us to visit his nightclub and I am happy to accept, sure that this will provide a nice diversion for Gail.

When he arrives to pick us up, I am astonished. In addition to the usual black shirt and pants, he is wearing a black Stetson and cowboy boots together with a low-slung ammunition belt and a holster with what appears to be a revolver poking out of it. There is a large silver star on his shirt.

He obviously enjoys the impression he has made and explains that his nightclub, "El Rancho," is in the western style. It occurs to me that "El Rancho" may also have been the scene of his skirmish with the police last year and I feel less happy to be going, especially with Gail. What kind of place is this? Is it suitable for a relatively inexperienced sixteen-year-old? Or even for her more experienced godmother? Whatever the situation, it is too late to back out now. Manuel would be offended.

He leads us in through a spacious saloon with tables and a dance floor, going past the bar, which is decorated with all manner of western motifs—coiled ropes, a buffalo head, saddles, bridles, spurs, etc.—to a patio at the back. It is cool out here, but nearby, on a raised hearth among the cobblestones, a fire is blazing. It is only ten o'clock and not yet crowded, but Manuel, chatty and amiable, a drink in one hand and the ever-present cigarette in the other, is in and out, dividing his time between us and the clients at the bar, and obviously enjoying himself tremendously as chief honcho.

During one of his stopovers with us, Gail tells him of her own connection with the West—one of her ancestors was a Texas Ranger whose gun she has inherited.

"Why, that is extremely interesting!" exclaims Manuel. "Please tell me about him." In the course of their conversation, it soon becomes clear that he knows exactly who the Texas Rangers were and, at one point, he even quotes their traditional description—"They ride like Mexicans, shoot like Tennesseans and fight like the devil."

"How come you know so much about them?" Gail asks in surprise.

"When I decided to have a western style nightclub," he explains, "I read all I could about the history and development of the West. First, I did not want to be caught making foolish mistakes in establishing and decorating the club and, secondly, things like that interest me. Besides, if somebody like yourself comes in who knows the West," he adds with gracious touch of deference, "I wish to be able to speak with them intelligently. Also, I love the outdoors and open spaces. It is my dream to have a ranch of my own one of these days."

Under Manuel's watchful eye, the service is exemplary—our slightest need is anticipated. However, the menu is all beef and, since I normally avoid red meat, I ask about chicken. The headwaiter, a well turned-out ranch hand, regrets that it is not available and his expression of barely concealed disdain suggests that it never will be—not if he can help it—so I relent. In any event, our steaks are grilled to perfection and, in spite of myself, I enjoy the meal. Now, wined and dined, we relax beside the fire.

It is pleasant out here, but the place is filling up, the noise level is rising, and Gail is attracting a certain amount of attention, especially from a group of rather authentic looking cowboys that have recently arrived—part of the floor show, Manuel explains.

After a meaningful glance in our direction, one of them saunters to the empty dance floor and begins to practice his rope tricks. It's an impressive performance and when he's through, Gail applauds enthusiastically. He bows mockingly, pushes his hat to the back of his head, rolls a toothpick from one side of his mouth to the other, and swaggers toward our table. Several of his companions ease off their bar stools and prepare to follow.

I feel uneasy. Atmosphere is one thing but this is *not* a ranch, we are *not* out west, and I don't particularly *want* these people to join us. I wish we hadn't come and I hope Gail keeps quiet about the Texas Rangers. Their leader has almost reached the patio when Manuel intercepts him.

"An excellent performance," he says placing a firm hand on his shoulder. "I see you are even more accomplished than your advance billing suggests. Now, let us discuss the timing of the show," and he turns toward the bar. There is a moment's hesitation during which I gather up my charge and prepare to leave.

Manuel sees us into a taxi and I breathe a sigh of relief. Gail is disappointed that we are leaving before the floor show and I don't blame her. On the other hand, I think we may have avoided some unpleasantness. Quite an evening, I reflect, and Don Manuel is certainly an interesting person. However, I have to marvel at the extent of my stupidity. How could I possibly have confused his extravagant game of make believe with the all too serious state of mourning. And what *has* become of his wife, I wonder?

In the News—
An Interview with a Bull

Today's paper includes a letter from a reader on the subject of bull fighting. He is responding to a previous article in which the European Economic Community directed some pointed criticism at Spain concerning this most sacrosanct of national pastimes.

The writer of the letter makes it clear that he is totally opposed to the sport. Nevertheless, he reasons, in fairness to all parties, it would be useful if one could interview a bull and ask him, "Given a choice, which of the following alternatives would you prefer?

"To be castrated at birth, confined to a small space, overfed, and, when you have reached the required size, taken to a sordid, foul-smelling abattoir, filled with bellows of fear and the stench of death and there be unceremoniously slaughtered; or,

"Would you prefer to be left with your masculinity intact, permitted to grow to maturity running free on the range and, at a certain time, be taken to an arena filled with music, color, excitement and, finally, participate in ritualistic combat with a high probability of dying?"

It would be interesting, the writer observes, to receive the bull's opinion on this.

The Beach and the Paseo

The sweeping crescent of beach below my apartment is one of three bays and one small inlet that comprise "La Playa de las Canteras" (The Beach of the Quarries), named for nearby, long unused marble quarries. A tiled promenade, the "Paseo de las Canteras," follows the contours of the beach for its full two miles and is an extremely important feature, not only of the waterfront, but of the whole city. There are probably very few of its 400,000 residents (not counting tourists) who do not come here from time to time to enjoy it.

Viewed from my terrace, the Paseo disappears around a headland of hotels and condominiums to skirt a rocky inlet with its own small patch of sand, known affectionately as "La Playa Chica" (The Little Beach). Another solid headland, the old Hotel Gran Canaria, and a second bay stretches out—still protected by the reef. Then, suddenly there is a change. The reef has ended and the third bay is wide open to the Atlantic. Huge crested rollers come crashing in from the west, hissing and foaming up the sand before spending themselves and sliding back under the surf. Out in the water, young men in wet suits wait expectantly to catch the perfect wave.

On its landward side, the Paseo is packed solid with hotels and apartment buildings, although here and there, tucked in among them, a traditional private home manages to survive—usually built of stone or stucco with a heavy oak door and balconies of dark carved wood. From one I regularly hear a rooster crowing, so somebody is really clinging to the old ways.

By law, buildings giving on to the Paseo are limited to seven floors, and each floor after the first two must be stepped back so as not to shade the beach. From above, they resemble so many pyramids, but from below only the two lower floors are visible which contributes to a pleasant feeling of openness.

The comings and goings on this busy promenade are constant and the people are from all over. Many are visitors, relaxed and in holiday attire, others are residents hurrying to work. Still others remind us that the Canaries are a mere seventy miles from Africa.

I think of these as "The Exotics"—they may be Arabs, elegantly tall Senegalese, or exuberant Ghanians and Nigerians. There is not much outward sign of hilarity among the Arabs. Serious brooding types—but with an unquestionable aura of romance, they stride along, white robes flying in the wind—Lawrence of Arabia and all that. And if you've ever wondered what they wear underneath—the old kilt question—well, it was a cool day when I caught a glimpse through a slit in the side and on that occasion it was a pair of slacks and a serviceable sweater. This could have been an aberration. Their wives, all wound round in quantities of diaphanous material which they clutch and rearrange as the wind conspires to whip it away, scuff along several paces behind them.

One Arab woman accompanies her small son to a corner, watches as he crosses the street, and continues to gaze after him until he disappears through the entrance to his school. An Indian man throws corn to a flock of pigeons while his sari-clad wife looks on. An Englishman greets a Spanish couple.

"And you've met Bosko," he says indicating his dog.

"Bosko!" exclaims the wife. "His name is not Sit!"

A group of black musicians—probably Ghanain or Nigerian from their wildly patterned clothing—laugh uproariously at some private joke as they load their station wagon with a variety of drums and other musical instruments—perhaps heading for a "gig" at one of the nightclubs in the south.

Of course, the majority of those passing back and forth are Canarios, but whether *true* Canarios, the product of countless generations in the Islands, or those they gently disparage as "from the Peninsula," is almost impossible to tell. Only those who speak the local dialect can be identified for sure. Their language, rooted in archaic Spanish, is often unintelligible even to other Spaniards.

One day in Las Palmas, I was in a taxi with a Spanish friend from Madrid. She asked the driver about a new highway being constructed and he launched into a lengthy explanation. I was discouraged not to understand, but my friend offered a sympathetic murmur once in awhile. When he was through, I asked what he had said.

"I haven't the slightest idea," she confessed.

I like to go out early in the morning when everything is freshly swept and the few people around are either joggers or walkers like myself. At this hour the restaurants are just beginning to arrange tables and umbrellas on the Paseo although one or two already have a first customer.

The tide is low this morning, and the lagoon inside the reef is glassy calm. Swiftly and silently, a kayak cuts through the water, skippered by an erect middle-aged woman in swim suit and shady, wide-brimmed hat. She paddles effortlessly and is soon far ahead of me.

Approaching me now are the three ladies in black—a mother and two daughters I assume—arm in arm, briskly in step, grim and unsmiling. I have been seeing them for years so the bereavement could not have occurred recently—will they never smile again? Perhaps he left everything to his mistress—like the shapely young woman swinging along in front of me in skin-tight designer jeans with a provocative glimpse of bare bottom through a horizontal slit—nicely frayed and probably self-inflicted.

And here, as usual, making his way slowly and painfully, comes the gentleman with a cane. At each step one leg flings out wildly but he gets it under control and continues the process with calm determination. I admire his courage, and instinctively straighten up and quicken my step, grateful for my own well-being.

Now, out of breath, but at a good pace and boisterously cheerful in their exercise suits come the German ladies—one bears a strong resemblance to Helmut Kohl. If this is a struggle to regain their long-lost form, I have to say it looks completely hopeless. On the other hand, they are obviously having a wonderful time making the effort.

It seldom rains in Las Palmas, but on this July day, the sun is obscured by a light cloud cover known as "Panza de Burro" (Donkey's Belly) and named for the animal's soft grey under fur. Not an unusual condition during July and August and welcomed by the locals since it keeps the place cool during the two hottest months, but a source of serious concern to visitors because it robs them of the 100 percent exposure they had counted on.

The other phenomenon that sometimes comes between them and their full measure of sun is the "Calina"—a wind from Africa that picks up sand and dust from the Sahara. By the time it arrives over the Canaries, the sand has been deposited but the dust remains, forming a light haze which can last for several days—driving sunbathers wild with exasperation and coating everything with a fine, white powder. During an infestation in Africa, the Calina even dropped a few travel-weary locusts along with the dust. Farmers were understandably concerned and on Las Canteras, sanitation men assiduously went about the task of raking up those brought in by the tide, many of which—hardy souls that they are—still showed signs of life.

In general though, the Canaries have a superb climate and have become a tourist Mecca for Europeans. During the winter, sun-starved Swedes, one of the most numerous groups, are quietly fanatical about absorbing the maximum amount of sun during their stay. A few wear colored plastic covers over their noses, which may have reached the limit of endurance, giving them the appearance of large prehistoric birds. Germans and English are also well represented on the tourist scene.

On Sundays and holidays, however, the local people repossess their beach with gusto. They arrive with everything needed to set up a home away from home—umbrellas, folding chairs, tables, etc., plus quantities of food and children. The latter are soon in and out of the water and since this is a safe beach everybody is relaxed about their comings and goings.

Spanish parents are loving, demonstrative and permissive—their children generally animated and high-spirited. A happy clamor soon develops, and rising above everything is the universal cry of "Mama! Mama! Mira! Mira!" (Mummy! Mummy! Look! Look!) as though nothing—whether it's going under for the first time or taking a few tentative strokes without the inner tube—is really worth doing unless one's mother is there to be impressed. Mothers range from young, sleek, and bikini-clad to veterans with protruding abdomens thrust out proudly like badges of honor to mark their many encounters with the mid-wife.

"Jaime," a father protests mildly to his exuberant son, "don't drown her—she's your mother."

Children line up to turn somersaults in quick succession on an air mattress. A circle of little girls sings—one carries the verses in a clear, sweet treble while the others keep up a rhythmic clapping and join in the chorus. Adults pass the time chatting, eating, playing cars or napping—a few even swim. A Gypsy woman, urged on by her companions, chants the traditional and always tragic "Cante Hondo." Further along, a young man with long hair and a guitar has his following. Radios are not permitted on the beach.

And all the while, waiters with food and refreshments scurry back and forth among the tables that line the Paseo. A woman studies the menu and asks a waiter if the fish is really fresh. "Señora," he assures her, "if you put this fish in water it would immediately swim away."

There are always several policemen on duty—serious, pleasant men whose principal occupation seems to be taking stray children into friendly custody until parents arrive to claim them. The present lost child is a blond female of about six, skinny, snivelling, and completely nude. Well, first things first—after all this is Spain, not Scandinavia or San Tropez. From a proper distance up on the Paseo, the policeman interrogates her, not about her parents, but concerning the whereabouts of her swim suit. A woman nearby, surrounded by a family of her own, tosses over a spare T-shirt which the child pulls over her head. This apparently satisfies her protector's idea of propriety, for he beckons her up and they set off hand in hand in search of family and friends.

Meanwhile, out on the lagoon, a half dozen wind surfers skim back and forth like giant, colored, flying fish—in sharp contrast to the higgledy-piggledy showing of a small armada of sailing dinghies manned by a class of ten-year olds, and critically observed from the beach by a weathered old salt guarding the fishing boats.

It isn't until around seven that an almost imperceptible exodus begins. It increases over the next few hours as families gather their things together and move slowly and reluctantly toward the exits. However, it never really succeeds in emptying the beach completely, for swimmers and sunbathers are soon replaced by groups of young men and women with volley ball nets, soccer goal posts, and a variety of other equipment, eager to claim any vacant space as it becomes available. Since the beach and the Paseo are flood-lit all night, it is not unusual, especially on weekends, for them to be still playing at one or two in the morning—this is Spain, remember!

On Sunday evening it is the Paseo that comes into its own. This is the place to see and be seen—the time to fix oneself up, put on one's best clothes, and stroll from one end to the other. People come from all over Las Palmas and even beyond. Little girls have ribbons in well-brushed hair. Formal shoes and socks have replaced the day's barefootedness. There's a stop at a beach-side table for aperitifs, and a visit to an ice cream parlor for the children. Teenagers eye one another speculatively. Couples stroll arm in arm or sit on one of the benches to watch the passing parade. "I am thirty-two," one confides to her companion. "Centigrade or Fahrenheit?" he inquires.

A sand sculptor has miraculously produced a reclining Medusa with snakes twined about her head. The result is extraordinary and he stands by with his assistant, savoring the exclamations of wonder and admiration, but keeping a watchful eye on the basket placed invitingly in front of him and now half-filled with notes and coins. Last week he did a lion attacking a fallen antelope with such skill that it seemed unthinkable that by next day it would all be gone.

And here on a small pedestal, is the one who makes a sculpture of *himself*. His whole body, including a carefully draped loin cloth, as well as his face and hair, are heavily gilded as he poses motionless for what seems an eternity.

A father holds up a skeptical child, attempting to convince her that this is, in fact, a real person. Trying to be cooperative, the "statue" squeezes her hand. She responds with a terrified shriek.

Now, I am back in my apartment and suddenly, on the Paseo below, there is barking, snarling, and shouting as a dog fight erupts. A boy of about twelve dives into the fray and hauls out his dog just as a policeman arrives. The officer proceeds to give him a dressing down—probably for not having the animal on a leash. The boy is plainly distressed and, perhaps to demonstrate that he is well in command of the situation, gives the dog a few sharp clouts as he clips on the collar.

As soon as the officer is through with him, he hurries away with his dog in tow. They round the corner of a building across the street and now, out of sight, the boy drops to his knees, wraps his arms around his pet and gives him a tremendous hug—no doubt apologizing for his shabby treatment a few minutes ago. The dog responds with an understanding lick and they trot happily off down the street.

As darkness falls and the crowds thin out, African vendors emerge at various points to spread out squares of patterned cloth and arrange their wares—carvings, finely wrought vessels of copper and brass, jewelry, embroidery, etc.—hoping to attract buyers from among the affluent dinner crowd.

Eventually, however, everybody is gone and quietness descends, to be broken only at intervals by the chatter and laughter of those making their way home from one of the many bars or restaurants. At last even that subsides, leaving the waterfront deserted for a few short hours until, out of the darkness, the first fishermen appear, heralding the start of a new day.

Omiros

As I am having dinner in the restaurant downstairs, a figure appears out of the gloom. Actually, his hair appears first—white-blond and softly waving to his shoulders. This, together with a matching beard, contributes to a rather Christ-like image. His style, however, is pure hippie, the elegant and expensive variety. He carries a portfolio of paintings which he is offering for sale. I find them interesting and invite him to have a cup of coffee while I look them over. They are signed "Omiros."

He tells me his is Greek. A few days later, when I see him again, he confesses that he only *wishes* he were Greek, but that he is actually German. He lived in Greece for five years but was deported for smuggling watches. His adopted name, "Omiros," is Greek for Homer.

He leaves early, explaining that his Swedish wife is returning that evening from Stockholm where she has gone to have an abortion. The next day, he tells me that she is not actually his wife but his girl friend. He rents a room from her mother.

In any event, I reflect, as I watch him striding along the promenade, blond hair and long scarf streaming in the wind, he is an unusual character and, a week or two later when a friend comes to visit, I think it would be interesting for her to meet him. I leave a message to let him know where we are having dinner.

During the meal a person with a portfolio approaches our table. I try to ignore him. However, when he speaks, I realize with astonishment that it is Omiros. He no longer has a beard, his head has been shaved and the hair bristling out is black. He is wearing a navy blazer and grey slacks with an ascot tucked into the collar of his shirt.

"I grew tired of that hippie type," he observes cheerfully, as he sits down. "He was beginning to bore me."

My friend, who didn't like his paintings anyway, wonders why I thought he was so special.

A few days later, he is to return to Germany. Before leaving he comes to say goodbye, and gives me his address in Dusseldorf. He explains that he will be living with his grandmother.

Around Gran Canaria—With a White Knuckle or Two

"Gran Canaria" ("my island"), where I live when in the Canaries, is more or less round with Las Palmas at the northeastern extremity. Notwithstanding its impressive name, one can drive around the perimeter of Gran Canaria in less than a day. However, as I studied the map, it occurred to me that I had never actually been all the way round and I decided to correct that situation. I even identified the part that I may have been subconsciously avoiding—a jagged black line of highway on the west coast between Agaete and San Nicolas which has been described as "terrifyingly scenic."

In any event, this morning I was up early to take the bus from Las Palmas via the northern route to Agaete and then to San Nicolas. From San Nicolas I will pick up another bus that will return to Las Palmas via the southern route and get me back around five this afternoon, having "done" the perimeter.

Despite its small size—approximately fifteen hundred square kilometers—Gran Canaria possesses an extraordinary variety of climates and scenery—sand dunes, magnificent beaches, and palm groves in the arid south, and a rugged interior with pine forests and formidable granite peaks that rise to more than six thousand feet. To the west these drop precipitously to the sea, but elsewhere give way more gradually to rocky foothills, undulating fields, and sheltered valleys.

It is through just such a landscape that I am passing on the first leg of my journey to Agaete. Rain is plentiful here in the north, valleys thick with the broad, clean leaves of banana palms or planted with almond trees, avocados, coffee, or grape vines. And here and there, blocks of cultivated flowers brighten the landscape—roses, carnations, chrysanthemums, etc., raised for local and overseas markets.

In Agaete, many of the passengers from Las Palmas disembark while others, bound for San Nicolas, take their place. Most are middle-aged women with packages and bags and kerchiefs on their heads, apparently returning from early morning shopping. One man stows some garden tools in the outside luggage carrier before getting on, while another, laden with plastic shopping bags, scrambles aboard, settles himself for the journey and crosses himself fervently. Come to think of it, they have all crossed themselves—more or less fervently.

I soon understand why. We have barely left Agaete before we are creeping around great rocky crags to which, somehow, the road has been persuaded to cling. Staring across a fearsome chasm at the makeshift character of the highway that lies ahead, I find myself wondering about construction methods in this part of the world—in non-technical terms, will it hold up? It is already clear that this is not a trip for the faint-hearted and equally clear that I am, in fact, miserably faint-hearted.

Thousands of feet below, I catch a fearful glimpse of the waves as they rock back and forth against the cliffs. The sky is cobalt blue, the sea is clear aqua as far as the coastal shelf where it merges into the deeper blue of the open sea. There are some truly magnificent views if I were not so busy helping the driver get this cumbersome vehicle around each impossible curve to enjoy them.

One of my problems stems from the fact that a large chunk of the bus extends well beyond its front wheels and, since I am seated in the right hand corner of that chunk, I get to hang over a precipice each time we round a bend—which is constantly. As we approach the most hair-raising twists our driver gives a blast on the horn and I soon find it better not to look. When there are two blasts, I make damned sure not to look.

Then, what I had feared occurs. An enormous truck rounds a bend and confronts us—bumper to bumper. Our driver pulls over, suicidally close to the edge in my opinion, and opens the door, which gives him a better view of the few miserable inches we have to spare and provides me with direct access to certain death. During the eternity—or longer—that it takes the truck to get by, I remain suspended in outer space. I am just about to give myself the last rites when the truck pulls clear, and our driver—my hero!—leans into the wheel, heaves on it with great muscular arms, and around we go.

Having survived that encounter, I feel encouraged to take a furtive look over the side. About half way down to the sea, the sun casts the shadow of the mountain above us. Along the edge of the shadow, I see something slither over a scattering of boulders. I watch curiously then realize it is the shadow of our bus making its puny way around the mountain. Here and there one can pick out the rusted skeleton of a vehicle that didn't make it.

I selected this particular seat to assure myself of a good view and now I am learning that sometimes there can be too much of a good thing. Of course I could move—there are other places available—but that would reveal to my fellow passengers that I am a craven coward—a fact that I am too cowardly to admit.

This, I reflect, is, indeed, a most barren and forbidding part of the island; arid, rocky, with only an odd patch of dark scrub—an uninhabited wilderness. Suddenly the bell rings! Faulty wiring perhaps? But the bus stops and the man with the plastic shopping bags struggles to the front and clambers out. On one side is the mountain, on the other a perpendicular drop of several thousand feet to the sea. Where can he be going? As we pull away, I crane my neck and see him trudging back along the shoulder. Then, far below, I glimpse a small figure, her dress whipped by the wind, moving slowly up toward the road along what must be a path, although she appears to be walking along a sheer ridge of solid rock.

We continue on our way and here among the crags is a patch of soil, mysteriously terraced and cultivated but with no house or any other sign of life. Some miles further on is another, but this time with a solitary man digging. He pauses and leans on his shovel to watch the bus. I wave. He doesn't seem to notice. I wave again. The shovel drops as he extends his arms high above his head and waves back exuberantly.

We cross a river bed, now completely dry but well-fortified with huge rocks cemented into place to contain what will probably be a raging torrent during the rainy season. Here and there groups of white-washed houses huddle together, usually with a palm or two rising high above them, very African.

And now I realize that scattered about, singly or in groups, the Pita is in bloom. It is a huge plant, spiny and succulent, and although I have always admired it, I don't remember seeing it with flowers before. From each cluster of broad leaves, a single elegant stalk—more like a small tree trunk—thrusts the flower head skyward some twenty to thirty feet, adding a wonderfully decorative note to the landscape. And some, growing down the bank beside the highway, provide an eye-level view of the flowers as we pass—white blossoms arranged with geometric precision on layers of horizontal branches.

Closer to San Nicolas there are larger and more frequent areas of cleared land. Here is an avenue of ancient cypresses set lonely and incongruous upon a barren hill. Perhaps they once led to a stately home. Now they stand like strange sculptures, eerily twisted by the gales that come howling across the Atlantic before racing furiously up these gullies.

Gradually the countryside takes on a more civilized appearance until finally, we are passing through extensive areas planted with row upon row of vegetables—beans, peas, cabbage, lettuce, carrots—all grown here and trucked to the cities.

Finally we arrive at San Nicolas, a spotlessly clean little town with cobbled streets and the narrowest of tiled sidewalks, the old section cramped and huddled about the cathedral. I should like to explore these twisted alleys but there is barely time for a quick snack before my bus is due to leave.

While I wait for it in the shade of a spreading Acacia tree, the one for Agaete pulls in. I am glad not to be taking it. It was a wonderful experience but once was enough—"terrifyingly scenic" was an apt description. When I make no move to get on, an elderly gentleman seated beside me on the stone bench begins to fidget and regards me anxiously. Finally, he leans toward me.

"Excuse me, Señora, but this is the bus to Agaete," he reminds me gently. Perhaps he had seen me getting off earlier and assumed I intended to return. I thank him and explain that I am waiting for the bus that goes via the south. He nods and settles back, evidently satisfied that he has done his duty and that I am not a poor, lost foreigner in need of assistance.

Leaving San Nicolas, we see the town, first from one side, then from the other, as we negotiate the succession of hairpin bends that leads out of the valley. There is a last glimpse of the breakwater extending far out into the sea before turning a protective arm around the port.

Then, more villages before we make our way through and around the crustation of tourist developments that cling to the southern coast—hotels, motels, apartment buildings, rows of identical villas, and busy shopping malls. Then a broad straight highway cutting north through the eastern plains—tomato country, acres of them grown for shipment to Europe—and finally, home.

"So, how was your trip?" asks Manuel.

"Wonderful! I wouldn't have missed it. But several times, between Agaete and San Nicolas, I was reminded that I am terribly afraid of dying." He laughs. "In addition to the spectacular views," I add, "the Pita is blooming and I had never seen that before."

"Ah, it is blooming now!" he exclaims, looking more interested. "You were very fortunate—and no wonder you have not seen it before. It will be four, maybe five years before this occurs again. Since their flowering depends upon weather patterns, all plants in a particular area bloom simultaneously, so they look quite exceptional of course. But they flower only once, scatter the seeds, then die. From the seeds a new generation will appear to wait another four to five years before repeating the process. So, you see, you did not risk your life for nothing."

In the News—Pubis de Oro
and Original Sin

A double header today—"Pubis de Oro" and "Original Sin."

Pubis de Oro: The final episode in a whole series of events involving a well-known member of the jet set. Several years ago she had bragged to anybody who cared to listen that she wore no underwear. Shortly afterwards, there was visible evidence of this when, dressed in a miniskirt, she sat in a night club with her legs crossed. A photographer took a picture and his magazine published it, pubic hairs and all. She sued. At the time I didn't think she had a prayer, but now, after several appeals, she has been awarded damages. Not the 200 million pesetas (around one and a half-million U.S.) she had demanded but a sizeable 34 million (about 250,000 dollars).

It is interesting, says the article, to see the difference between the value which the lady places on the area between her legs and the amount she received. Apparently 200 million seemed exaggerated to the judge who probably took into account the fact that this is a fairly common part of the human anatomy found in approximately half of the world's population.

As in other cases, the article continues more seriously, we are faced with the question of the rights to our own image. Does it belong exclusively to us or does it also belong to the beholder? The young lady had not been pursued into her own bathroom, which clearly would have been a violation of her privacy, but was photographed in a night club—a public place.

The question of violation of privacy would not have arisen, the article goes on, if she had just worn pants, but then she would not have 34 million pesetas. A record price for a glimpse of anybody's pubis—many millions more than a whole generation of strip tease artists would have received and for a much better view.

Original Sin: A political satire in which Adam, alone in the Garden of Eden, becomes "bored as an oyster" and God has this brilliant idea to provide him with a companion. As the writer observes, the rest is recycled history.

When Eve arrives she can hardly wait to get at the apples and is bitterly disappointed to find they are off limits, having been placed on the list of endangered species.

Adam, being something of a wimp, is prepared to abide by the rules. But Eve, anxious for Adam to make something of himself, considers the ban unfair and even discriminatory. She also suspects that God, having created Adam in his own image, may be having something of an identity crisis. Furthermore, she has come to realize that Adam is not all that bright and perhaps, she reasons, it may also be part of the "Grand Design" to keep him that way. With an improved I.Q., who knows what problems he might cause. For instance, he might want to change some of the rules or, heaven forbid, he might start getting ideas about who should run the place, and before you know it, there goes the neighborhood.

Eve, on the other hand, is confident that a taste of the tree of knowledge would be just the thing for Adam. So, after considering the pros and cons she slips a few slices of apple into his salad, assuring him it is part of his diet— low in calories and good for his cholesterol.

Naturally somebody squeals and all hell breaks loose. She and Adam are banished from the Garden forthwith. Nothing daunts Eve, however. In her new place—the first recorded shelter for the homeless—and with nothing further to lose, she dedicates herself to promoting the consumption of apples. She creates recipes for apple pie, apple tart, apple crisp, apple turn-overs, and apple dumplings, to name just a few, all of which she regularly serves to Adam and the children.

And today, the earth is filled—half-filled at any rate—with the daughters of Eve serving apples in various forms to their spouses on the same old pre-text—that they are low in calories and good for their cholesterol. And their husbands, fully aware of what is going on, accept them meekly and secretly revel in the sins of their distant ancestor.

So Adam did, indeed, make something of himself as Eve had hoped and his name certainly has gone down in history—recycled or otherwise.

The Struggle

Manuel has invited me for lunch at a steak house owned by two of his former protégés. They trained as chefs in his restaurants, he tells me.

"Ah, here is Enrique," he says as we arrive.

"Good to see you Don Manuel. You have not visited us for some time. We miss your advice."

"He means criticism," Manuel says dryly before introducing me.

We have a corner table, which is fortunate because, by the end of the meal, Manuel is in a rare mood to talk about himself.

"I believe I have told you," he says, as we linger over coffee and he lights a cigarette, "that I come from Córdoba—except that it is not really Córdoba, but a small village on the outskirts. 'El Cordobez', the famous bull fighter, also comes from that village, but he was barely a teenager—fighting cows as a matter of fact—when I left to do my military service. That was after the Civil War. At that time, two years military service was compulsory for all males when they reached the age of eighteen.

"And, although I despise Franco, he did a good thing when he introduced general education into the army. He realized that many of those young men, like myself, had very little formal education. When I should have been in school, for example, the Civil War was in progress and, after the fall of Córdoba, my father, my brothers, and I spent the next several years until the armistice hiding for our lives in the mountains. Even after surrendering, Loyalist men and boys were routinely shot by Franco's troops. This was to prevent uprisings and to protect the rear guard of the army. Once in a while, and at great risk, we would sneak down to see my mother and get food and I would also try to catch a glimpse of the girl who would eventually become my wife.

"In the army, I took every course they had to offer and for me this opened up a new world. First, I was surprised by my own aptitude, proud to see that I excelled most others. Of this was born the hope of making something of my life. But perhaps more important, it gave me a thirst for knowledge that has never left me and from that time I have never ceased to study. At whatever time I go to bed, and over the years it was often at daybreak, I have developed the habit of reading for one hour—history, economics, philosophy. It has become one of my greatest pleasures, and I also make a point of becoming as well informed as possible concerning whatever project I am engaged in.

"In any case, by the time my unit was sent here to Las Palmas, I had become a sergeant and it was here that I took my discharge. Las Palmas was very different in those days; a population of perhaps one hundred thousand and extremely poor—but all of Spain was poor at that time—much of it devastated, and I felt there might be better opportunities here, much better than in Córdoba, for example.

"I was able to get a job in a restaurant and I watched and I learned. Then I found an additional job in the factory of a Swedish carpet manufacturer. That man helped me a great deal. I am from a very poor family, the second youngest of seven brothers, and it seemed the buck always passed down to me. I was pushed very hard, and now I am glad. It was good for me. Besides, I appreciated so much when I no longer had to deal with it.

"Anyway, this Señor Bergsen took a real interest in me. When you are young, the fact that somebody really cares about you makes a tremendous difference and a word of praise can change your whole life. A person may say 'How well Manuel did that' and suddenly you say to yourself, 'So, in that case I must be something special' and you are encouraged and have more confidence—you are *somebody*. He also urged me to study English, which I did."

"And you also speak Swedish. Did you learn that from him?"

"Some of it. Later I took lessons, and for very practical reasons: An increasing number of Swedish tourists were beginning to arrive. In any event, I was given more responsible jobs, saved my money, went back to Córdoba, married my childhood sweetheart, and brought her here."

"Soon, a friend and I scraped together everything we could and started a restaurant. We worked very hard and it did well. Before long, I also had a nightclub. After a few years I built a small hotel. By this time the tourist industry was booming and in 1970 I decided to build 'Casa Manuel'. That was a good investment and it has also done well." He pauses thoughtfully, stubs out his cigarette, and lights another.

"The problem is," he continues. "that I am now completely overburdened by my own success. I have *too* many things to do, *too* much responsibility."

"Can't you delegate some of this to other people?"

"I have tried to do this but it never works. And with 'Casa Manuel', the restaurants, the nightclub, and the hotel, I am always pushing myself. There is never enough time for everything. Sitting here with you, for example, I am thinking of things that need to be done, so I feel restless, almost guilty, and that is ridiculous."

"But surely, after working so hard for so many years you have earned the right to relax a little and enjoy yourself without feeling guilty about it."

"One would think so. But this is the irony of it. When you have to struggle too hard to make something of yourself, even when it becomes clear that you have succeeded, you are unable to stop struggling—to struggle has become a part of you." He pauses, then continues. "Perhaps the solution is to make a clean sweep and sell everything—maybe leave the Canaries altogether."

"Where would you like to go?" I ask. He looks helpless, a little lost.

"I don't know."

As we rise to leave, he fixes a disapproving eye on a waiter serving at the next table.

"He reaches in front of a patron," he says, shaking his head in disgust. "Either he has not been properly trained or he should be fired. Not only is this unprofessional and discourteous, it can also lead to unnecessary accidents. Where is Enrique?" he asks looking around, "I must speak to him about this."

Getting There
Is Half the Fun

"Don't push the lady!" admonishes the teenager. We are waiting to go through security for the flight to Madrid and his companion has bumped me with his back pack.

"Sorry," he says, flushing with embarrassment.

"That's okay. You two off to Spain?"

"Sí," answers the first.

"To study?"

"Sí," says his friend.

"Well, it's obvious that you both have an excellent command of the language so I'm sure you'll do well." They explode with laughter and pummel one another.

When their turn comes they pass through without incident but I set off the entire alarm system. I am invited to step aside where I am frisked and gone over with a small mine detector. All this under the curious gaze of my fellow passengers ("What do you suppose she's got in there?" "Doesn't look the type, does she." "Can never tell."). Just as I am beginning to savor my notoriety, security attributes the problem to an excessive number of hair pins and sends me on my way.

I slump into a seat in the waiting area, tired from the things I had to do before rushing out of the house, relieved that it is now too late to worry about those left undone, and a little ruffled by my recent experience as a suspected terrorist. Not to worry—soon I can relax on board with a drink, then there'll be dinner, and I may even get a few hours of sleep.

But it is not to be. When we board it is announced that the cabin crews are on strike. On my seat is a plastic bag with a note advising me that this is dinner and breakfast. It contains a variety of stuff—cold cuts, salad, rolls, cookies, juice, etc., as well as cream and sugar for the coffee which will never materialize, and an apple. I scratch about for the small bottle of wine that I just know the airline must have tucked in somewhere to make up for all this.

It's not there of course and I only succeed in dropping the apple which rolls away and disappears under the seat in front.

"Please take mine," says my neighbor. I decline, but he insists—which is a big mistake, because this turns out to be the best part of the meal.

"You'd think they might have given us some wine," I grumble.

"Yes, I wondered about that. Maybe they thought if we had too good a time we wouldn't miss the cabin crew."

And, as I reflect upon it, I may not miss them. The cabin crews on the New York/Madrid flight are senior staff who have obviously become bored to death with the whole miserable business. The only time I have seen them even crack a smile was when somebody dropped a tray on a passenger. And one elderly attendant bears such a striking resemblance to Pope John Paul it's embarrassing to see him doing the rounds with the coffee pot.

In any event, apart from the fact that nobody is bothering me to have a vodka and tonic or taking forever to serve dinner, which I have eaten before we get off the ground, I soon discover several pluses connected with their absence—to wit, nobody is distributing and collecting head phones which I never use; or doling out socks which I never wear; and, even more important, there is no movie, which I never watch, and I actually get more then the usual amount of sleep. So, except for vodka and coffee—which I could always bring along—I would be just as happy to make do with my plastic bag of air rations, and a pox on the cabin crew, thank you very much.

Actually, when I travel by plane it's the location of my seat that is most important to me—window, non-smoking, and as far up front as possible.

I like to be beside a window, not because of the view, but because particularly on a night flight, I can tuck myself in and sleep undisturbed. I like to be near the front so that I can get off quickly for passport control and baggage claim, or in case of some "unexpected stop"—which I try not to think about. Also, if things get bumpy, I find it reassuring to be near my surrogate father, the gentleman with the deep voice—"This is your captain speaking."

So, if I can reserve my seat in advance I do so at the first opportunity and, if I have to wait until check-in time, I'm there when they open. Invariably, therefore, I get what I want. Then all I have to do is hang on to it. For example, there was the man with the carrying case who needed my seat for his dog. No dice. And the young lady who warned me that if she didn't get to look out of the window, she might very well throw up—she didn't actually say all over me, but I got the picture. In any event, she didn't get to look out of the window and she didn't throw up, which was nice.

This time my seat is occupied by a woman studying some distant horizon.

"Sorry to disturb you," I venture, "but I believe you're in my seat." She turns and rattles her bracelets at me.

"This," she responds indignantly, "is where I was *told* to sit," and gives me her back. It takes the flight attendant to get her out.

28

"I," she announces from her seat on the aisle, "am supposed to be in *first class*. If they hadn't overbooked I would never be *back here*." A stint in the tourist section is obviously not her idea of "The Great European Adventure."

Then there was the time I, myself, had to settle for a seat on the aisle. During the night, as I lay swathed in blankets, the person in the middle tried to get out without waking me. In the dark, he took a firm hold of an object blocking his way and attempted to lift it up, not realizing, until I lashed out, that it was my foot. I must have kicked him in a sensitive place, because he sank back into his seat and remained crouched over as though he might be hanging on to something. I tried to apologize, but he kept his head resolutely averted as though he never wanted to look at me again—ever—and he seemed to have lost all interest in going to the bathroom or wherever it was he was headed. I was quite upset about the whole thing. So much for a seat on the aisle.

I arrive in Madrid in my usual daze following a night flight. It's 7:30 A.M. local time, 1:30 A.M. in New York—way past my bedtime. After some groping about, I eventually find the gate for my flight to Las Palmas and two hours later we are all on board. A missing passenger is paged on the public address system but there's no response. Finally, the doors close and I assume he missed the plane.

We move out toward the runway, then stop abruptly and nothing happens. Shortly afterwards, from my window I see a red van approaching. It says "EMERGENCY" in large letters. I feel the need to communicate this piece of information to somebody and turn to the man beside me.

"There's an emergency vehicle down there," I remark pointing. He shrugs nonchalantly and returns to his newspaper. "Perhaps there is a bomb scare," I suggest.

"Oh, come on!" he responds derisively. A few minutes later several baggage trailers arrive, along with another emergency vehicle. This one has a large wire cage on the roof. I report these events to my companion. Now he seems more interested.

"They are unloading our baggage," I announce. He looks downright alarmed.

"It could be that there is a bomb on board!" he exclaims—as though he had thought of this all by himself.

Now officials are examining the identification tag on each piece of luggage before setting it aside. As I report these matters I have my companion's undivided attention.

Finally, "This is your captain speaking" comes on the PA system and explains that, after we taxied out, the computer showed we are carrying a piece of luggage checked in by a person who was ticketed but did not board the plane—the one who was paged before our departure, no doubt. Since he cannot be located, the article he checked in must be found and off-loaded as a precautionary measure. Everybody understands perfectly what "a precautionary measure" implies for this is the classic method of getting explosives aboard.

Down below, the sorting and checking continues and now, several figures gather around a suitcase. No jaunty tuft of colored ribbon adorns the handle so it's definitely not mine. Gently they place the suspicious object into a large metal container and wheel it ever so carefully to the van with the wire cage. Then it is driven off, probably to some remote area for further examination. At this news, my companion murmurs fervently and crosses himself.

We eventually take off, three hours late. How fortunate, I reflect, that I had a window seat, otherwise, I would have been sitting for three interminable hours without a clue about what was going on. And when we arrive in Las Palmas, I discover that whatever evil designs anybody may have had on our plane, I, myself, was clearly and unequivocally above even the slightest suspicion since *my* suitcase, although checked all the way through, had been left behind when I made the transfer in Madrid.

I Disapprove of
Siestas—Zzz Zzz Zzz

In the Canaries, as in other parts of Spain, the siesta is on its way out—or so they assured me before I left New York. Business establishments are gradually conforming to the hours observed by other European countries, they explained—especially now that Spain is a member of the Common Market, they added. After all, one can't afford to be asleep when somebody calls from London or Brussels, can one?

Very good, I thought approvingly. I, myself, am firmly opposed to siestas—"naps" we call them. I prefer to go to bed at a reasonable hour, get a good night's sleep, and get up early in the morning. I enjoy the mornings. So, if the Spanish are coming around to my way of thinking, so much better. Following my arrival, I even leave my watch on New York time, so as not to get too far off my regular schedule.

On my first evening, around 8:00 P.M.—an hour later than my usual dinner time in deference to local custom—I look around for a restaurant in which to take my evening meal. There are crowds of people at tables *outside* the restaurants chatting and sipping *aperitivos*, but the rows of tables inside are spotless and unoccupied. I take a stroll along the Paseo and back.

9:00 P.M., and still no sign of dinner being served. Footsore and faint with hunger, I select a hospitable looking cafe, slink by the animated pre-diners, seat myself in an inconspicuous corner, and keeping my voice down, order an omelette.

At 10:30 P.M. I am back in the hotel preparing for bed. The doorbell rings and I throw on a robe. It is Manolo and his wife from next door.

"Oh, you're getting ready to go out," he says, sounding disappointed. "We wanted you to have dinner with us." Too bad I have already eaten. It would have been much more fun to have had dinner with them. I avoid mentioning that I am getting ready for bed.

By 11:30 P.M., it is past my bedtime. My room overlooks the beach, which is floodlit at night and as I climb into bed, I am uneasily aware that very small children are still tearing about playing games. I smooth down the covers and compose my thoughts for sleep.

At midnight, I am just dozing off when there is a thunderous clanging and crashing, as if the building is being demolished. I spring out of bed. Outside is a cavernous garbage truck into which are being hurled all manner of bottles and cans. The clamor recedes and I return to bed.

At 12:30 A.M., children still at play. A continuous roar gets me out of bed again. A massive street-cleaning machine, accompanied by a man struggling to control a high-powered hose, is proceeding slowly and deliberately about its business. It disappears into the night leaving everything glistening and dripping wet.

At 1:00 A.M., there is an animated discussion beneath my window. By 1:30, things have calmed down. Even the children have vanished—probably having dinner. So finally, I can sleep. But wait, another piece of heavy equipment is being brought up. It looks like a bulldozer but turns out to be a beach cleaner. For an hour it drones back and forth, dredging and sifting the day's debris from the sand. Finally, having taken the entire coastline apart and put it back together again in neat contiguous strips, it trundles off.

By 2:30 A.M., apart from numbers being called at a nearby bingo parlor, all is quiet. I finally doze off around three o'clock. A creature of habit, I am awake at my usual 5:30 A.M. *Well,* I tell myself as I stumble out onto the balcony, *You're on vacation. Today you can take it easy and tonight you'll make up the lost sleep.* It is beautifully quiet now. Only the waves washing up on the sand break the silence, and, except for a fisherman making his way noiselessly toward his boat, the beach is deserted.

At 7:30 A.M., I go out to the Paseo which extends for two glorious miles. The smell of the open sea, the cool breeze, and the worn tiles smooth beneath my feet give me a wonderful sense of well-being.

By 9:00 A.M., I am back at the hotel. I order breakfast in my room and take it out to the balcony. Everything tastes delicious.

At 11:00 A.M. I go down to the beach. I am feeling a little weary now—last night's activities are catching up with me. A trickle of people begin to appear—mostly Spanish families on vacation, all looking extremely well-rested. The water is cool, clear, and wonderful. I emerge refreshed and stretch out in the sun. A young man approaches and asks the time. Since my watch is small and I am not wearing my glasses, I first have to get it into focus. Then, since it is still on New York time, I have to add five hours, and since I do my calculations in English, it is necessary to translate the result into Spanish, all of which takes time. My friend fidgets impatiently and attempts to look at the watch. To avoid further confusion and explanations, I cover it up. Visibly offended, he turns on his heel, just as I have the answer to his question. I call it after him, but he seems not to hear. He is probably asking himself why foreigners have to be so impossibly rude—what chance is there for world peace?

By 1:00 P.M., I am showered and dressed for lunch. At this hour the dining rooms are immaculately empty and not even the aperitivo crowd has assembled. Rather then buck the system, I decide to do a little shopping and make my way to an embroidery shop. It is closed. Seeing my disappointment, a kindly passerby explains that all shops close between one and 4:00 P.M. So much for the Common Market. I return to the restaurants. Aperitivos are now in full swing, but there is still no sign of solid food. I don't want an aperitivo. I don't need one. It is way past my lunch time and I am starving. Finally I saunter ever so nonchalantly into a nearby restaurant and seat myself at an outside table overlooking the beach. A waiter appears.

"Si, Señora?" he asks.

"Could I possibly have some lunch?" I beg quietly and apologetically.

"But of course," he replies in a conspiratorial undertone. The fresh fish is lightly broiled and delicious. I wash it down with a carafe of white wine.

I return to the hotel. The bed looks extremely inviting. According to my watch it is 11:00 A.M., but I change it to 4:00 P.M. local time. I wake up at six. I have succumbed to the siesta—and it feels marvelous!

Then There's the Language Barrier

Apparently, the author of *Useful Words and Phrases in the Spanish Language* does not consider the word "death" to be all that useful. "I am about to vomit" is there—although I can't remember the last time that happened. And "kindly remove your hand from my knee" is also there—although, as a matter of fact, I can't remember the last time that happened either. But "death" is not even mentioned.

So when I try to call my building administrator who, unbeknownst to me, has had a fatal heart attack, there is a series of misunderstandings. When his secretary informs me that he is "fallecido" I have no idea she is telling me that the man has died.

"Well," I say, determined not to be sidetracked by whatever it is he has, "I want him to know that a faucet in my apartment is leaking—after all this is an arid country and I feel very strongly about not wasting water."

"I understand, Señora," the young woman says patiently "but Señor Gonzales is fallecido." There was that word again—"fallecido"—it sounded vaguely familiar but I couldn't quite place it.

"Excuse me," I say in my best Spanish, "but I didn't understand. Señor Gonzales is what?"

"He is fallecido, Señora."

"I see. Well, when do you expect him back?"

"Señora, he will not be coming back. I am telling you, he is fallecido." Then it strikes me! I didn't take two semesters of Latin for nothing. "Fallecido" sounds as if it must be connected in some way with "phallus." Could his absence have something to do with sex? It is only eleven o'clock in the morning, but in a country where people regularly dine at midnight, who knows what kind of schedule they have for other things.

Or, could it be that he is having a *problem* with his phallus? Maybe "fallecido" is a condition—like tendinitis. You get that from *using* a tendon too much. I should know—I once had tennis elbow. In any case, I am determined not to give up—what he does in his private life is his business

34

but one simply cannot disregard the water problem.

"Well," I ask, returning to the attack, "do you think he will be back tomorrow?"

"No, Señora. He will never be back."

"Never! He's resigned perhaps?"

"No," she says with a touch of desperation, "he did not resign."

"He's out of the country then?"

"Señora, he is not only out of the country, he is out of the world." Did she say "he's out of this world?" The woman's obviously infatuated with him.

"I see. Well, thank you very much. It's been *so* nice chatting with you—and if Señor Gonzales *should* return, would you be kind enough to ask him to give me a call?"

Spaniards are more accustomed than Anglo-Saxons to touching one another—and this doesn't mean a pat on the fanny. They seem to derive comfort and pleasure from the physical presence of one another. Parents caress their children a great deal, a husband often walks with a hand on the shoulder of his wife, men hug one another. It is not surprising, therefore, that during a conversation between an Anglo-Saxon and a Spaniard, the Anglo-Saxon is constantly edging away in order to put a respectable distance between them while the Spaniard continues to move closer in an attempt to diminish the gap. So, at a cocktail party, I am not surprised to find myself doing the "pasadoble" with a fellow guest.

"I see the back of your head and say, I have to meet that señora," he says, standing uncomfortably close. I step back and smile knowingly. He edges forward and glances at my wedding band.

"Married?" he asks.

"Yes." Back.

"Your husband—does he feet you?" Forward.

"I beg your pardon?" Back.

"Does your husband feet you?" he insists, edging closer. I am not sure what "feeting" involves but it sounds a little off color and I am preparing to tell him that it's none of his business whether my husband feets me, when it occurs to me that he is saying "fit you," which can be roughly translated as "suit you." Still a rather intrusive question, and actually, my husband happens to be in New York at the moment doing his best to divorce me, but I don't think this gentleman's vocabulary is up to a discussion of that. Not wishing to embarrass him by drawing attention to his mistake, I tell him, "Yes, my husband feets me quite nicely thank you."

"I think you have many thoughts," he speculates darkly. "Perhaps you are too sentimental." A big step forward.

"As a matter of fact," I respond casually, holding my ground this time, "What I am is oversexed." He hesitates, skeptical but definitely interested.

"Say again," he urges with an eager step forward that puts us belly to belly.

"Sorry," I respond, taking my final step backwards, "but I must go now. I have to meet my husband and if I am late he will have a feet."

Here's To a Long Life!

Out on the Paseo I see Abbie heading toward me. Abbie, I would guess, is around sixty, tall, angular, and so erect she appears to be leaning backwards. Her grey hair is gathered in a careless topknot, leaving a strand or two draped across her forehead, and her clothes are loose and ill-fitting, but she carries herself with the assurance of a general inspecting her troops. A fixed smile fails to conceal a certain underlying bitterness.

Over several years, as we have passed and repassed during our morning walks, a flicker of recognition has gradually led to a greeting and then to the occasional chat. I learned all too soon about the unhappiness in her life. She and her husband came to the islands from England so that she would have time to write and he could pursue business opportunities. Apparently that was not all he pursued because, before long, he left her for a Finnish woman.

When she first described how he had been lured away, her fury and indignation were such that I assumed this had occurred during the past week or two and I was full of sympathy. Later I was astonished to discover that these events had taken place almost twenty years ago. The hurt had been carefully nurtured to as to be almost as good as new.

Occasionally, while we are talking, she will catch a foreign word or two from a passing woman and break off what she is saying to listen intently, ready to turn on the hate if what she hears happens to be Finnish. This morning, however, she looks unusually cheerful.

"I just did my good deed for the day," she announces proudly.

"Really! What happened?"

"As you know, I sometimes go over to the port to see which ships are in." Yes, I do know and I consider these forays somewhat foolhardy.

The Port of Las Palmas, just a few blocks from the Paseo but on the other side of a narrow isthmus, is the busiest in all of Spain and hums with activity—ships being refueled and provisioned (as were those of Columbus on his voyage of discovery); others in up-to-the-minute dry docks for repairs; cruise ships waiting to disgorge throngs of tourists for a day of sightseeing and/or shopping (the islands are duty free); fleets of ocean-going fishing vessels from as far away as Korea. All of which contributes to the overall vitality of the place.

Ports, however, inevitably have their down side and there are the usual reports of drug trafficking, violence, and muggings. Abbie scoffs at my warnings and maintains that the area is the safest place in the world. So far nothing has occurred to change her mind and I sometimes wonder if this has to do with the fact that she marches around looking so unassailable that, over time, she has become so.

"The only new arrival this morning," she goes on, "was a terrible old hulk—probably in for repairs—so I didn't pay much attention to it. But, as I walked along the dock between the ship and the street, I noticed a book lying beside the curb. It was dirty and battered and had lost its cover but, as a writer, it pains me to see a book discarded so I felt compelled to pick it up. I turned a few pages and saw that it was in Chinese, so I didn't understand what it was about of course. Then I realized that it seemed to be divided into sections, each with a roman numeral. This suggested that it might be a manual or a text book of some kind. Also, it had a number of pencilled notes in the margins— again in Chinese.

"Since it had been directly across from the gangplank of the ship, it occurred to me that a crew member might have dropped it as he got out of a taxi. So I went over. Nobody was around. Then a rather grubby cabin boy appeared carrying something that looked like a chamber pot. I tried to talk to him but he didn't want anything to do with me and scurried off.

"Finally, a man came on deck—a rather sinister-looking character—who looked as though he could be an officer. I held up the book and pointed to where I had found it. He seemed to get the idea and beckoned me to come aboard. I didn't think that was such a good idea."

"Abbie, how cautious you're becoming!"

"Yes. Advancing years I suppose. Anyway, he came ashore. We exchanged a few remarks which neither of us understood and I gave him the book which he accepted with signs of appreciation, but not excessive. Well, I thought, at least I've done what I could and started back.

"Then, after awhile, I heard the sound of running behind me and some urgent hissing. I stopped and there was this young man hurrying toward me. When he caught up to me I saw that he was clutching the book. Well, he babbled and laughed and pressed his palms together and bowed deeply and repeatedly. Obviously, its return meant a great deal to him. I said, 'I'm so glad I found it' which, of course, he didn't understand, but at that moment, in spite of so-called barriers of race, culture, and language, we were in perfect communication. Then we turned and went our separate ways.

"So, it sort of made my day," she concludes. I am pleased to see her so happy.

"Abbie, you really did do a good deed. Maybe he was studying for an exam. If so, the loss of his manual could have made the difference between success and failure—especially with all his notes in it."

"Yes, after I left him, I thought the same thing as a matter of fact." Then she says, "George (that's her husband) was at the house yesterday. It was the christening of our first grandchild."

"Wonderful! Congratulations!" I exclaim.

"Thank you," she responds. Then her face falls into its normal unhappy contours. "George's arthritis has become so bad he has to walk with a cane," she observes.

"Oh, that's a shame," I reply guardedly.

"My daughter tells me that 'she' (her husband's companion is never referred to by name) is not doing so well either. Heart problems—has a pace maker."

"She" had obviously not been a passing fancy. After twenty years they are still together and might have been married except that Abbie would never agree to a divorce.

"Well," she says reflectively, "I hope they both live to a good old age." Finally, I think gratefully, Abbie is coming to terms with the situation. "That way," she adds "they'll have plenty of time to see one another disintegrate," and she turns abruptly and leaves—a tall solitary figure, nursing her private hate as she threads her way among the crowds of light-hearted vacationers.

El Parque Santa Catalina

Set in a busy shopping area, the park is a small magnet of a place swarming with vendors and crowded with tables and umbrellas where both tourists and locals gather to eat, drink, and chat. Traditionally, there has been an ongoing battle for supremacy within the park and its environs between legitimate business and the police on the one hand, and drug dealers, petty thieves, and prostitutes on the other.

Since my last visit to Las Palmas, the park has been renovated to within an inch of its life. The jumble of stalls that sold everything from fine leather handbags to glow-in-the-dark condoms has been cleared out. Illegal extensions constructed by surrounding restaurants have been torn down. The whole place has been repaved. Areas of new turf have been added. Trees have been carefully encircled with protective stonework. Freshly-planted flower beds are in full bloom. The evil-looking pond which had become known as "Lake Peepeecaca" has been restored to its original pristine condition and additional toilets have been constructed in the hope that it will stay that way. There is a gratifying sense of beauty and order—at least on the surface.

The young woman loitering to one side does not look the type to be waiting for her mother and that other one, all frills and curls and false eye lashes, may be just too feminine to be the real thing. A man, sleek and shifty-eyed, strolls casually through the crowd. Suddenly he stoops and appears to pick something up. It is a thousand peseta note (about $10) which he holds out to a tourist.

"Señor," he says with a disarming smile, "I believe you dropped this."

"Oh, thank you very much," the tourist responds, grateful and pleasantly surprised as he accepts it. He takes out his billfold—and in a flash it is gone as the thief races off with it.

Encounters—The Painting,
Los Adorables, and
At the Bank

The Painting. From time to time I paint and suddenly I feel a creative urge. I decide to produce a small masterpiece to hang over the couch in my living room. Filled with enthusiasm I have a wooden stretcher made and buy and piece of canvas, treated with something that smells so horrible I am not sure I should even let it into my apartment. However, neither the shop where I buy the canvas nor the one that makes the stretcher can be persuaded to attach one to the other and I do not have the necessary equipment to do it myself. Somebody suggests I take them to a nearby art gallery.

The man in charge readily agrees to take care of it. I can pick it up tomorrow.

"Wonderful! How much will it be?"

"That I cannot tell you."

"Well, but just approximately."

"I do not know," he says firmly, looking me in the eye. Perhaps he is an assistant who is not permitted to give estimates. On the other hand, it sounds like a rip off.

The next day when I arrive, the canvas is well stretched, the corners perfectly tailored, and the edges trimmed precisely—a beautiful job. It also becomes clear that the man I dealt with is the owner of the gallery.

"How much do I owe you?" I ask, prepared for the worst.

"Nothing," he says matter of factly.

"Nothing! But surely it can't be *nothing*," I say, thinking I may have misunderstood.

"Yes. Nothing. It was a pleasure to do it for you, Señora."

"But this is a lot of work. It is beautifully done and it obviously took a lot of time. I must pay you something," I insist. He smiles patiently and shakes his head. I thank him and leave, thoroughly ashamed of my suspicions.

It would be nice to say I think of this gracious encounter whenever I look at the painting. Unfortunately, my work of art, so breathtakingly beautiful in my head, bears no relationship whatever to the disaster that finally takes shape on the canvas—now pungent on two counts. I think regretfully of my generous friend as I consign it to the trash can, being careful to secure the lid against art critics and the local cats.

Los Adorables. My neighbor's two small children—aged about two and three—have made an interesting discovery. They have found, that if they push a small round button outside my door, an extraordinary thing happens: The door opens and a woman appears—a sort of female Jack-in-the-box. I have become such a fascinating phenomenon that they push it at every opportunity. While their frantic mother restrains one, the other dives over and gives it a jab. When I appear, which I do less frequently as time goes by, she is terribly embarrassed and full of apologies.

"Ah, 'Los Adorables'," I observe reassuringly.

"Si, 'Adorables'," she repeats grimly as she hustles them through their door.

As I relax on my terrace I hear the parrot next door—or is it a man whistling at me who sounds like a parrot? I take a furtive look. It's the parrot.

At the Bank. For the first time I am about to deposit a check in my Canary Island bank account. I search among the various forms at a long table provided for the public and finally select one. As I study it, I must look as perplexed as I feel, for a hand reaches over my shoulder and gently takes it away. Another hand reaches for the check which I meekly surrender. Quickly and efficiently the owner of the hands, a young man in his twenties, scans the check, fills out the deposit slip, hands them back, and, with an indulgent smile motions me to stand in front of him at the teller's window. Except for my thanks and his courteous acknowledgment, we haven't exchanged a word.

The Friday Group

When the phone rings the day after I return to Las Palmas, I am reasonably sure it is Virginia. She always asks when I will be coming back and is usually the first to call. Sure enough it is her shy, timid voice bidding me welcome and telling me that this week the Friday Group will be at Irene's. It is already Wednesday and I am happy to have a ready-made gathering to attend almost at once.

The "Friday Group" is a collection of compatible individuals who get together every week to exchange news and gossip over drinks and tapas. Nobody seems to know exactly how it got started and it had been going for many years when I was invited to join. Actually, I wasn't really "invited" to join—it was more subtle than that.

I was asked to come for drinks at the home of a friend. "Friday at noon," she said. Several couples and a few singles, mostly English, drifted in until we were probably about twelve. Although I didn't realize it at the time, this was the "Friday Group." When we broke up, I, apparently having measured up to some unspecified standard, was invited by next week's hostess to come to *her* home and, after several weeks of going to various houses, I felt bold enough to suggest we gather next time at my place and that is how I became a fully accredited member.

When I arrive on Friday, most of the others have already assembled and there is a round of welcoming hugs and kisses. Irene has set out generous platters of hors d'oeuvres and is now dispensing drinks—"Pinkies" (gin and bitters) and "whiskeys" (never "Scotch" since, for the British, nothing but scotch whiskey exists).

Virginia, the one who called me, is prim, delicate, and as always, faultlessly turned out. Her husband, Mathew, had already died when I joined the group and she shares an apartment with Pauline, the pretty one sitting beside her, also a widow. They appear to live in perfect harmony although it has been rumored that there have been a few violent arguments, one of which even led to blows. I find it difficult to imagine two such perfect little ladies having at one another but one never knows—especially after a Pinky or two.

One day when Virginia and I were alone, she said in her little-girl voice, "Did you know that Mathew and I were never actually married?"

"No, I didn't," I replied, slightly taken aback.

"No, we never were," she said thoughtfully. "But," she added, "we lived together for thirty years which was just as good don't you think?" I said, truthfully, that I thought it was even better. Thirty years ago, house-mates, or consorts, or live-in companions were not as fashionable as they are today and, to live together openly and out of wedlock must have required more courage than I gave her credit for.

There's a ring at the door. It's Diana. She apologizes for being late but explains that it was all Jeffrey's fault. Jeffrey, her husband, hasn't come to our gatherings since he and Diana stopped speaking three years ago. According to some unwritten agreement, Jeffrey is supposed to shower, have his breakfast, and vanish from the apartment by the time Diana returns from her early-morning walk. Today, for some reason, their system of moves and countermoves didn't work and he was still in the shower when she came back.

"I had to delay my breakfast," she complains, "and it ruined my entire morning." Irene hands her a Pinky.

"Drink up, lamb chop, and pretty soon you won't feel a thing."

Georgina, a pale wisp of a thing with violet eyes, reminds me how much we all miss Aaron—a cheerful, capable man who not only took wonderful care of her but of the rest of us as well. If anybody needed help to install a T.V. or a stereo, locate a leak in the plumbing, or diagnose a strange sound in their car, Aaron was their man. When he and Georgina entertained he even took charge of the cooking.

When Aaron died, Georgina was not only devastated but ill-prepared to cope with the world by herself. For example, she had never before written a check and a bank statement was a complete mystery. Aaron had dealt with everything.

One of the more important things she had to do was sell their house. She listened patiently to advice showered upon her by anxious friends, and then went about her affairs quietly and privately. To everybody's surprise and relief, she sold it well and at a good price. Unaided, she then searched for an apartment and bought one in a most desirable neighborhood at what we all considered a snap. She sold four of the five apartments they owned in a tourist area immediately before the bottom dropped out of the tourist industry—and to an Englishman who was able to pay in sterling, thus avoiding taxes and currency restrictions. The remaining apartment she rents out or uses to entertain her family when they come to visit.

"Aaron didn't think I could do anything," she mused one day. "He even wrote his own obituaries before he died, he was so sure I would make a mess of them. You know," she added with a twinkle, "for a person who was not supposed to know which end was up, I think I've done quite well." And I had to agree whole-heartedly.

43

The stately one with the piled-up grey hair, long earrings, and chunks of jewelry scattered about is Meridian. With her bright colors, sweeping skirts, blouses that somehow manage to slip off one shoulder, and shawls that trail after her, she is not easily overlooked—nor does she intend to be.

Meridian—we suspect she may have rechristened herself—is a self-proclaimed Pantheist. In the past she has demonstrated excerpts from the ritual that serves to keep her at one with nature. It consists of a series of postures and incantations performed at sunrise, preferably in a natural setting. Since she lives in an apartment on the tenth floor she does them on the terrace with one foot in a container of earth. At the moment she is asking what the hell is being done to stop the government from raising our taxes.

"I believe," she proclaims, "this country was *vastly* better off under Franco. Don't you agree?" she challenges first one then another. "Couldn't agree more!" "Absolutely!" "Knew where we stood!" "Locked them up if they didn't toe the line!" Since I do not share these opinions but wish to avoid a confrontation, I slip into the kitchen and find Irene already there for the same reason. We have a quiet giggle as we wait for the quiz to end.

Humphrey is here today without Thelma, who is in England visiting her mother. Last week he had boasted that he was getting along famously without her and didn't understand why women made such a big thing about a little housekeeping. But that was last week and she'd only been gone three days. Yesterday he cut his finger with the can opener, the kitchen sink clogged up, a TV dinner got welded to the inside of the microwave, and he's depressed. We remind him that in a few more days Thelma will be back to put an end to his suffering with her unimportant little household duties.

Meanwhile, Catherine is sitting very erect and listening attentively but, as usual, not saying much. She and Peter were the perfect couple—attractive, cultured, great golfers, excellent bridge players, and accomplished cross-word puzzlers: he did the *London Times* puzzles in his head so as to leave a clean slate for her. We always thought it was a pity they had no children, especially when Peter died a few months ago and their wonderful relationship ended.

Suddenly there is a pause in the conversation which she uses to claim our attention.

"I have some news," she announces in her direct way, this time with her jaw slightly outthrust. We wait expectantly. "I've never discussed this before," she begins, "but thirty-five years ago when I married Peter, I left a husband and two children—three and five years old." We are stunned.

"It was all very unpleasant," she continues dispassionately, "and there has been no communication whatever with them or with my former husband since that time. However, after Peter's death it was necessary for me to make a new will—and I thought of the boys. My lawyer needed to know if, in fact, they were alive and, if so, where they were, so he set about tracing them." We are hanging on every word. "He discovered one in England, the other in

Kenya, and got in touch with them. Immediately afterwards, to my astonishment, I received wonderful letters from them with photos of themselves and their families, and begging me to visit as soon as I could." She is as close to tears as we have ever seen her—but they are tears of pure joy. Then out comes a bundle of photos and we pounce on them.

Here is Henry, the eldest, a handsome man of forty, with an attractive wife and two teenage sons; and Philip, now thirty-eight with a twelve-year-old daughter and an infant son, the product of a second marriage, Catherine explains.

"So I'll be leaving for Kenya in February," she is saying, "and during the summer there'll be a month in England with Philip and his family." We are misty-eyed. She had lost Peter but in his place, and beyond all expectations, has rediscovered two sons eager to know the woman who vanished from their lives so many years ago—to say nothing of four beautiful grandchildren.

There is a hubbub of questions then, "Heavens!" somebody cries, "It's past two o'clock!" "Closing time" is strictly observed and we rise hurriedly, say our thank yous and goodbyes, and wobble happily out into the day, too well-fed to enjoy the prospect of lunch, but with an uneasy feeling of not having had a proper meal—and finally, too tiddly to care. Perhaps ready for a nice nap. The English "nap." They do not take "siestas", which sound slightly off-color.

Carnival!

A week before Carnival the pulse of the city quickens and, above the usual clamor, a certain rhythm begins to emerge. The "Murgas" have arrived! These are the bands that will perform during the seven days of Carnival and now, a week beforehand, they are engaged in wildly enthusiastic competition to decide which will perform at the main events.

Preliminaries take place at local parks with crowds cheering, dancing, and singing from around ten in the evening until sunrise. Finalists appear on consecutive nights at the stadium with everything suitably amplified so that not a single resident in the entire metropolitan area needs to feel left out. At this point the whole city begins to throb and you had better get into the mood or get out of town.

When I went to pick up my breakfast rolls this morning, I noticed that Conchita, a pretty girl who works in the bakery, had a new hair-do, and that she was even more animated than usual. I admired her hair and asked if she were looking forward to Carnival.

"Oh, yes, Señora," she replied breathlessly, her eyes sparkling, "this is the best time of the whole year."

"Have fun," I called as I left. She giggled and nodded vigorously.

Carnival itself kicks off with the gala selection and coronation of the queen. As always, she is extremely beautiful and her costume is unbelievably spectacular. In fact, the outfits of all the candidates are so elaborate and with such enormous head-dresses that sometimes one has to search for the person within. I am told that participants undergo several weeks of serious physical training to prepare them for the task of supporting the weight of all this finery.

By contrast, for many of the other young ladies cavorting about town, especially during the procession, a glorified "G" string and a couple of stars seem perfectly adequate, although they too are apt to have great outcroppings of feathers and fronds at the head and wrists and other inconsequential places.

Could that be *Conchita* in that abbreviated outfit doing the Lambada or something equally provocative? As she winds it up she catches my eye and dives for cover, laughing.

The Parque Santa Catalina is a focal point during Carnival and this year the park is dressed to the nines for the occasion. In addition to the usual streamers, balloons, and strings of lights, great serpents, vividly colored and beautifully crafted, twine about the palm trunks happily tempting the revellers to further excesses. And, set up at intervals, huge folding screens made of some reflecting material less dangerous than glass provide an opportunity for all who pass to catch a glimpse of themselves.

Carnival is for setting aside one's problems, kicking up one's heels, and the hell with it. In the process, night and day become almost indistinguishable. Work hours are shortened even at the banks, but absenteeism reached such a level this year that the city almost came to a complete standstill. At the bakery this morning, the owner's wife was helping out and Conchita, whether by arrangement or default, was nowhere to be seen. I thought it better not to ask after her.

Revellers fill the streets at all hours and almost everybody dresses up. Men seem to be especially taken with the idea of impersonating women, as long as the transformation doesn't leave their masculinity in doubt. For example, one of a group of "nuns"—since Franco nothing is sacred anymore—thoughtfully puffs on a pipe as "she" fingers her rosary and another sports a black handlebar moustache.

Yesterday, middle-of-the-week day, was an official holiday and this morning Conchita is back. Not the pre-Carnival Conchita, however. The hair-do has collapsed and she looks pale and tired.

"Conchita," I ask anxiously, "do you think you're going to make it through Carnival?"

"Si, Senora," she replies firmly, but with more determination than enthusiasm.

In Tenerife, our neighboring island and all-time rival, carnival has become such a splendid affair that it appears on television throughout Spain and even beyond. Las Palmas, on the other hand, will never be ranked as having one of the great carnivals of the world—it's much too busy having a good time to worry about such essentials as organization and timing. Here, Carnival reaches out to the people and gathers them in with a big hug not even noticing whether they are well turned out or not.

This becomes especially clear during the "Cabalgada," the procession through the streets that is the culmination of everything. In Las Palmas, it takes anywhere from four to five hours to pass and it is a big joyous free-for-all. Floats are interspersed with groups of musicians and dancers on foot and these are interspersed with whoever feels like dressing up and getting into the act. The quality is variable to say the least and there are almost as many taking part in the parade as watching it.

There is the queen's float, elaborate and beautifully decorated, and there are other spectacular floats designed and constructed at great expense and filled with lavishly costumed occupants. But here comes a small truck decorated with strings of tinsel and a few palm fronds but holding a family singing and waving and having the time of its life—definitely not the stuff for national television. And now, what at first appeared to be two men impersonating a donkey turns out to be a donkey wearing two pairs of men's pants and a straw hat. And there, jiggling along to great applause is Charlie Chaplin. And over here, attracting her own share of approval, is a mother pushing a pram decorated with streamers and balloons and with another small child in tow.

Then, inching along between a group of Caribbean dancers and a float advertising the local beer, comes a truck filled with street cleaners—whether part of the parade or just taking the most convenient route to a clean-up job is not clear. They look self-conscious standing there in their bright orange coveralls and the crowd regards them silently. Then an official detaches himself from the reviewing stand, hurries over and is hoisted aboard. With broad smiles and much backslapping he shakes hands all around. The crowd bursts into applause. The cleaners wave back sheepishly and trundle on their way. In Tenerlife they would have been hustled off to a back street long ago. Meanwhile, children along the route scramble excitedly for a seemingly unending supply of candy tossed to them from those in the parade and a camel who has decided to lie down is hoisted gently to its feet and persuaded to continue.

However, not even Carnival can banish all problems. Posters throughout the city urge the population to take necessary precautions against the ever-present danger of AIDS. In the spirit of the festivities, one of these depicts a colorful and extremely animated rooster with a well-rounded attractive hen using her wings to place a condom over his beak.

Sunday, the day following the big parade, is reserved for the "Burial of the Sardine." The origins of this ritual are said to be ancient and pagan—catch-alls that save hours of time-consuming research. For this occasion the diminutive sardine takes on truly enormous proportions. This year's thirty-foot gilded monster could easily be mistaken for a genetically altered whale.

Crowds, slightly jaded at this point, make a last valiant effort and gather along the route to applaud as it is drawn through the streets to the funereal beat of drums and the clash of symbols.

And there among the onlookers, smiling, starry-eyed, and now typical Canary in a finely embroidered blouse and layers of skirts and frilly petticoats, is Conchita! At her side, a protective arm about her shoulders and paying no attention whatever to the sardine, is just about the most handsome young man I have ever laid eyes on. Well! So she made it through Carnival after all—and with flying colors. Anyway, back to the fish. Finally it arrives at the beach where it is transferred to a barge, towed a safe distance from shore and, to the accompaniment of a barrage of fireworks and much cheering and clapping, set on fire.

Whipped back and forth by the wind, flames leap high into the air. Gradually they diminish and the crowd quiets down. As the last flicker collapses sputtering and hissing into the water, Carnival is definitely over. Slowly the crowd disperses, the city heaves a sigh of fatigue and fulfillment, and everybody prepares for a good night's sleep.

Involved—To the Hilt!

As usual on Sunday evening, the Paseo is crowded. Threading my way home among the strollers, I notice a small black-and-white fox terrier. She means to be noticed. She is running back and forth, peering anxiously at the faces around her and barking impatiently—"Hey! I'm here! I'm here! Where *are* you?" Apparently she has become separated from her owners.

She's a jaunty little thing with a black patch that covers both ears and one eye, spotlessly clean, obviously well-fed and not to be confused with the "abandoned" dogs one encounters all too frequently in the city. I imagine she will soon be reunited with whoever she is looking for.

The following morning I am surprised to see her again and in almost the same place. She is circling a concrete pit at a construction site. There is a brown paper bag in the bottom, probably with the remains of some food. The pit is three or four feet deep and I am afraid that if she jumps in she may not be able to get out. After sizing up the situation from various angles with her head cocked first to one side then the other, she seems to arrive at the same conclusion because she turns and trots off. But every once in awhile she pauses to sniff something in the gutter. She's obviously scavenging and I am concerned.

I make a detour to pick up my breakfast rolls. As I return I look back and she's there in the middle of the street outside my apartment building. I stop and so does she. She regards me uncertainly. I call her and break off a piece of one of my rolls. She advances cautiously. I would like to get her off the street so I extend it and move backwards toward the sidewalk. I arrive at the curb sooner than expected and fall flat on my back. Unfortunately the sidewalk has been recently washed so my white pants and T-shirt are a mess. I express my chagrin with the choicest words at my command and scramble to my feet. She watches this performance impassively.

I am still clutching the piece of roll and pull myself together sufficiently to offer it again. She gives it a noncommittal sniff and backs off. I remember that a neighbor regularly puts out milk and cooked rice for the local cats. There is a half-full dish in the niche where she leaves it so I bring it out. This too is sniffed and rejected—cat food yet! I sense that she may be in trouble and speak gentle words of sympathy to her in Spanish. She watches me intently squinting her eyes as though she might be about to cry. Then she turns and trots off purposefully as though she has a particular destination in mind.

"Dios mío! What has happened to you?" It is Manuel, who has entered the lobby behind me.

"I fell backwards trying to coax a little stray dog off the street."

"That is terrible! What a disgrace that they are permitted to roam about the city. Something should be done about it," he observes severely.

Later in the morning I go out—this time armed with a can of dog food but with little hope of seeing her. In fact, as I round the first corner there she is—standing in the street in front of the Hotel Imperial. This is a dead end, so the cars that come here are usually destined for the hotel, then turn and leave. Each time a car comes she watches expectantly, scrutinizes the occupants, then retreats to the curb.

I approach and show her my can. Not interested. But as I squat down and begin to open it she becomes extremely interested. The doorman obviously does not think much of these goings-on at the entrance to his hotel so I move to one side and dole out the food onto a piece of plastic. She eats ravenously. The doorman comes over and appears to be sympathetic.

"I wonder how she came to get lost," I say.

"She didn't get lost," he replies. "She was abandoned. It was yesterday. I saw them do it. They came and turned around, ready to leave. Then the man took her to the Paseo and dropped her over the wall onto the beach. By the time she found the steps to get back up, they were gone. If I had realized what was happening I would have taken their number. She's been waiting ever since for them to come back."

"What a miserable trick! She's such a lovely little dog. How could they do that to her?"

"It happens every year at vacation time. People have nowhere to leave them and they just put them out or do what this couple did."

"I wish I could take her but that's impossible. Besides, there's just a week before I'll be leaving. Perhaps if I call 'Lassie'—the organization that finds homes for stray dogs—they could come and get her. In the meantime, if you would be kind enough not to chase her away, I will tell them where she is and they will know where to find her."

"That would be good. Otherwise the police may pick her up. In that case she would be sent to the pound and probably be destroyed."

"Oh, no!" I am horrified at the idea. "That would be terrible."

Meanwhile, the subject of our concern has finished almost the whole can of food and seems to have had enough. I offer my hand. She touches it with her nose. I attempt to pat her. She curls her lip. I respect her feelings and let her alone.

I notice an ugly welt on her rump that wasn't there this morning. At that moment one of the workmen from the construction site passes and she flees, cowering in terror. She's a spunky little dog, so he must have hurt her badly. He's climbing a ladder and I *will* him to fall off, but it doesn't work. As I leave I am happy to see the doorman placing a plastic bowl of clean water near the curb.

Back at my apartment I call "Lassie" and leave my name and number on their answering machine. Nothing happens. I remember that Marta, who cleans for me, had a dog that died a few months ago. Perhaps she would take this one. She explains that she now has two cats. I assure her that Tipper—that's what I have named her—would adore the cats but she is not convinced. Call "Lassie" again. Marta calls. No response.

Perhaps Manuel would help. As the owner of an apartment building in the area, a request from him should carry some weight.

"Manuel could you help me get that little dog off the street?" His expression is not encouraging. "If you could just call 'Lassie' and tell them she is outside the Imperial Hotel and ask them to come and get her. I have called and Marta has called and the people at the hotel have also called but nothing has happened. I am sure if you call they will pay attention."

"You give me more credit than I deserve," he replies bowing slightly. "I doubt that it would help. I am very fond of dogs but it is not a good thing to become involved in these things. I am afraid I cannot help you."

"Bastard!" I didn't even breathe the word but his antenna may have picked it up because he pauses and gives me a hard stare.

"As you know," he adds, "dogs are not permitted in this building."

"I am well aware of that," I respond curtly. "Rest assured, even if they were permitted, I would not bring her here. It would be too cruel to give her a home if it could not be a permanent one."

The following morning I take another can of food for her. She is in the same place in front of the hotel, patiently waiting for the family that has no intention of returning.

An elegant lady, who turns out to be the receptionist, comes out and, although clearly sympathetic, I have the feeling that both she and the doorman would like me to get Tipper out of there as soon as possible. Luxury hotels do not welcome stray dogs hanging around.

I have an idea. I call "Lassie" again, but this time I mention that I should like to make a donation to the organization. That does it. That evening I am visited by the president of the association, a charming young aristocrat obviously devoted to her cause. She wishes to explain the purpose and merits of the organization but I cut her short and hand over $120—the annual membership fee which I privately consider extremely high—especially when translated into pesetas. Well worth it though, I assure myself, to get Tipper a new home.

I lead María Dolores outside. Within the last half an hour I have seen Tipper twice from my terrace going down the ramp from the Paseo to her post at the hotel. Now, however, there is no sign of her. "Yes," says the doorman, "she was here just a few minutes ago."

"Don't worry," María Dolores assures me, "we will come in the morning—early, around 8:30—there will be fewer people."

The following morning I wait outside for them. I have not fed Tipper so that I can tempt her with food if it becomes necessary. By ten nobody has come so I go back upstairs and call. María Dolores explains that somebody is out with the station wagon and has not returned.

"I'm sorry we kept you waiting," she says. "We will come and get her this afternoon."

I explain that she seems to be dividing her time between the hotel and the Chinese restaurant at the top of the ramp on the Paseo.

"Okay," she assures me, "we'll check both places."

I have to go out during the afternoon and when I return Tipper is gone. I am a little sad but relieved to know that she is now safe and sound. I sleep better that night. The next morning when I go out for my walk, she is checking cars in front of the hotel. I am bitterly disappointed. Another call to "Lassie." No reply. I leave an indignant message. María Dolores calls.

"We came," she explains. "She was at the Chinese restaurant but as soon as we approached she ran. We drove around for half an hour looking for her but she was obviously hiding. Fernando (her assistant) will come in the morning. He will call you before he leaves." I wait all morning. No call. I go to the hotel. No Tipper. She is at the Chinese restaurant sleeping under one of the tables out front on the Paseo. I offer some food. She eats a little, but half heartedly. Is she sick, I wonder.

"My mother already fed her," says the teenage son as though this has become routine.

"I think she has adopted you," I say hopefully.

"Yes, but we have not adopted *her*," he responds firmly.

"Why not? She's a beautiful little dog."

"We already have a dog—ours is a pedigree."

"Well, she's no ordinary dog," I tell him. "You can see how alert and intelligent she is and how carefully her tail has been cropped. It's obvious that she also has a fine pedigree." Which may or may not be the case but at this moment Tipper needs all the help she can get. Besides it has occurred to me that she could come into heat and attract a pack of male dogs. That would really bring the police with their nets. I have seen small females being pursued and gang-raped by ragged monsters on the Paseo and heard their cries of pain. I cannot allow that to happen to her.

"We cannot have another dog," he says flatly.

Next day when I pass the restaurant, Tipper is lying in front of the entrance, head erect, ears cocked, paws extended parallel in front of her, for all the world like a small sphinx. Then the father emerges and a surprising thing happens. She wags her stump of tail furiously, leaps joyously into the air, runs in circles at his feet, feints and doubles, and leaps again.

"She's crazy about you," I observe.

"Yes," he says smiling placidly, "and when I leave here at night she follows my car all the way to the park." I am horrified. The park is at least a mile away.

"She could be run over!"

"Yes," he agrees without emotion.

"Why couldn't you leave her in the restaurant at night? She would be a guard."

"It is against the law to have a dog in a restaurant." So, at night Tipper is left alone on the street. I have an idea.

"She obviously adores you," I tell him. "If I bring a carrying case could you just pop her into it?" He shakes his head dubiously.

"I have never touched her," he explains. "I handle food and she is now very dirty." Which, unfortunately, is the case. What had been sparkling white is now a murky grey. The are only two days left before my departure and I am becoming more and more discouraged. That evening Fernando calls.

"Since you have become such good friends with the dog," he says, "why don't you just pick her up and bring her here yourself?"

"She won't even let me pet her," I tell him. Then I think about it. Why not try.

Next morning I map my strategy. I have no leash but perhaps I could wrap her in my beach towel. Then I could take a taxi to Lassie's head-quarters and everything would be solved. Since she is now being fed regularly, ordinary dog food would probably not appeal to her so, in addition to the beach towel, I take some cocktail sausages.

She is lying out front in the sun. I settle myself on a step and spread the towel beside her. I offer a sausage. She sniffs then wolfs it down. The daughter of the family emerges and unhesitantly bends and rubs her head. Thus encouraged, I offer another sausage and make some overtures. She allows me to stroke her. I rub her back and talk to her. She evidently enjoys this and turns on her side. I edge her toward the towel. She turns on her back, paws in the air in an attitude of complete trust, and I betray her. As I attempt to pick her up and she realizes she has been tricked, she shrieks, bares her teeth, and slashes in every direction. I am bitten on my arms and both hands before I have sense enough to release her.

Patrons are concerned and I am embarrassed by the scene I have created. She doesn't go far. Just stands off to one side regarding me reproachfully. I gather up my cocktail sausages, drape the beach towel over my bloody clothes, and retreat.

As I arrive at my apartment building, the person I wish to see least in the world is on his way out. Manuel's eyes widen as he sees the blood.

"Dios mío! What has happened to you?" he asks full of concern.

"I tried to pick up the little dog and she bit me," I snap defensively.

"It seems you will never learn," he says, concern changing to exasperation. Then, concerned again, "Are you badly hurt?"

"I haven't had an opportunity to look."

"Come," he says guiding me to his office. "Sit down," he orders as he takes out a first aid kit. "Now, where did she bite you?" I put aside the towel and extend my arms and hands showing the cuts—clean little slices as from a razor blade.

"What about rabies?" I ask, trying to sound casual as he takes out a bottle of peroxide and some cotton. "Should I see a doctor?"

"Fortunately, there are no rabies in the Canaries so that will not be necessary. If this had happened elsewhere you might not be so fortunate," he adds severely as he swabs the cuts with peroxide, and I try not to wince. He applies band aids to several of the deepest bites which are still bleeding. "You should swab them several times a day," he advises as he gets up. I am dismissed. It is perfectly clear that he does not wish to hear anything further on the subject of Tipper.

"Thank you, Manuel. That was very kind of you and I am relieved to know that I don't have to worry about rabies."

"Not at all. I am glad I could be of assistance," he responds stiffly.

I leave an indignant message for Fernando, describing my aborted attempt to capture Tipper.

"*You*," I tell him when he calls, "are supposed to be the expert in rounding up dogs, not I, and I think it's time you *did* something about it."

"I will talk to María Dolores and get back to you," he says.

In the morning when I pass the restaurant I stop to talk to the son.

"The man from 'Lassie' came yesterday," he says.

"What happened?"

"He asked me to help him. He wanted me to put a choke collar on her. I refused. If he puts a choke collar and she fights she will get hurt. I told him he should have a harness."

I go home disgusted with everybody. The next day I am returning to New York and the thought of leaving Tipper abandoned in the street and possibly ending up in the pound is almost unbearable. How come this small dog has such a grip on my emotions? I like everything about her: her appearance— jaunty and self assured—her courage, her independence, her sense of fun and her loyalty. She still takes care not to neglect her post outside the hotel, trotting over regularly to make sure nobody is waiting for her, and watching the cars as they come and go. The more I see of her, the more difficult I find it to imagine how anybody could abandon her. If it were not for the account of the doorman I would not believe it. María Dolores calls. She sounds contrite.

"We are leaving this minute," she announces. I am waiting downstairs when they arrive. She looks young and attractive driving her station wagon with "Lassie" emblazoned on the side. A friendly policeman ushers her into a non-parking area. She emerges wearing a pair of well pressed khaki overalls and a stylish, broad-brimmed hat—the very model of noblesse oblige.

"A few minutes ago she was outside the restaurant asleep under one of the tables," I vouchsafe. I notice that María Dolores has a leash—and that it is a harness.

"I would put that out of sight," I advise. "She is very intelligent and if she sees it she will run."

The policeman comes with us. She is still asleep under the table. With the confidence of one supported by the full authority of the law, he advances without hesitation, and before she realizes what is happening, has slipped the harness over her head. However he is unable to fasten it underneath. At that moment the son appears and she takes refuge between his legs. He bends and rubs her ears reassuringly. The policeman calls to Fernando to come fasten the harness.

"You go," I urge María Dolores and she does. In a second it is done and Tipper, after a few futile tugs, realizes that further resistance is useless. The son hurries inside on the verge of tears. María Dolores shows me a bloody hand but there are obviously no hard feelings.

"In a few days," she says, "she will be just as sweet and affectionate as you could wish."

When we arrive at the station wagon Tipper leaps nimbly aboard and settles herself in the corner of the back seat as though that had always been her accustomed place. Now it is I who am almost in tears.

"If you don't find a good home for her," I stress, "keep her for me. I will be back in December."

"I have a waiting list," she assures me. "She will have a wonderful home."

"Be careful whom you choose."

"I will be very careful. I will let you know when you return."

As I turn toward my building, I see Manuel at the entrance observing all that has been going on.

"It might have been better," he says "if you had not intervened. She seemed to have been accepted by the Chinese family and eventually they would probably have taken her in."

I am furious with him—not because of his meddling, which in any case, I could do without at this stage, but because his opinion exactly reflects my own doubts. For now that I have accomplished what I set out to do, I am troubled by the outcome. Apart from the fact that she has become dirty and badly needs a bath, I have to admit that she was not doing too badly for herself. She had become attached to the Chinese family and they to her. They fed her regularly and were affectionate with her. The only thing they would not do was give her a permanent home and they were maddeningly logical and seemingly implacable about it. In time, perhaps Tipper would have won them over. But there had not been time. I comfort myself that she is in safe hands and I trust María Dolores to select a good home for her. Manuel is still waiting for my response.

"You may be right," I reply coldly and hurry inside to dry my eyes.

I have wondered many times how Tipper fared but I never again got in touch with María Dolores to find out.

The Fishermen

There was a big to-do on the beach yesterday. The police had some of the fishing boats hoisted on to trucks and carted away. There were angry protests and some confrontations.

"We are taking only boats that are not registered," the police insisted, "or those which are no longer used."

This morning there is a photograph of all this in the newspaper together with a statement by a member of the City Council saying that the boats were taking up too much space and were being cleared "to give the beach back to the people." The next day I notice that a section previously occupied by fishing boats had been roped off by a nearby yacht club for some of its own small boats and equipment. A sign says "sailing instruction," giving the impression that this might be a public service but I doubt it. The clubhouse is close by so I go over.

"My son would like to take sailing lessons," I announce. "What is the procedure to enroll?"

"Oh, this is only for members, Señora," he replies, looking down his nose.

So I dash off a letter to the newspaper asking why, if the beach is "being given back to the people" a private organization, namely the yacht club, is permitted to reserve a large part of it for its own use? In a few days the letter is published and shortly afterwards the enclosure is removed. I am delighted and report my success to Manuel. He receives the new without enthusiasm.

"The fishermen should be moved to some other place," he says impatiently.

"Moved! Why?"

"Because they are a nuisance. They congregate on the Paseo; many of them drink too much; they quarrel and argue which creates a bad impression; and they clean their fish down there, which brings flies. They would be better somewhere else."

"I hope they will never be moved," I retort indignantly. "These are the *real* Canarios—they have character and personality. And tourists certainly enjoy them—you only have to see how they crowd around their boats when they come in. As for flies, I hardly ever see a fly."

"You don't understand very well," he says as though I might be slightly retarded, "in addition to the problems I have mentioned, people go down among the boats at night to take drugs and have sex."

"The boats are in full view of my apartment," I protest, "and I have *never* seen anything like that."

"Perhaps you do not wish to see," he replies, going off in a huff.

I have a lot of sympathy for the fishermen and I do not like the way they are being nudged out. These are men whose families have been here for generations. Weathered, and with a permanent squint from peering over sun-drenched waters, most are middle-aged to downright old—some even physically uncertain. They live in brightly-painted houses bunched together on "La Puntilla," a rocky point that juts into the sea just a short block from my apartment. With the open sea on one side and the sheltered northern curve of the beach on the other, La Puntilla is one of the most beautiful locations in the area. And when I say the houses are brightly painted, I mean that a purple house may sit next to one that is kelly green with a good, deep orange one on the other side—pastel they are not.

As I stroll past their enclave, a group sits in the shade of a narrow street. Some are playing checkers. One is painstakingly ruling lines of rigging into a pencil sketch of a steam ship he has drawn. A few minutes later when I return he is coloring in the funnels with a crayon. Another, watched attentively by a woman and a young girl, is painting the inside of a dinghy. There are no young men to be seen.

Fishing, a traditional and time-honored calling, obviously does not appeal to the young. Not too surprising for the work is demanding, a continuous struggle—not always won—against the elements and the vagueries of the open sea, and the rewards are uncertain.

Those sons who do follow the tradition because the sea is their blood, maybe even in their genes, do so as members of the crew of ocean-going refrigerator vessels that are away for weeks or even months on end scouring the high seas for their catch, and returning to tie up at the port on the other side of the island. That life is also hard and sometimes dangerous, but at least they are paid regularly and there is some hope of advancement.

My end of the beach, sheltered from the wind and with ready access to the open sea through a break in the reef, has by far the largest collection of small boats in the area. They are crowded together on the sand directly below my terrace, some right side up, others face down, some on stilts, others left to recline carelessly on their side, some covered with tarpaulins, others left to cope with weather and tourists as best they can.

And, just as the houses on "La Puntilla" are painted in every conceivable hue, so the boats also reflect the Canarios' love of color. "Tababa" is white above the waterline, blue below with a green interior. "Carmen"—a bit dilapidated—is off-white with green and yellow. "Antonia" is purple, green, and salmon-pink. I can make out one "Nina," two "Francescas," and a "Teresa," each contributing its own splash of color and, just as I am thinking that this is an all-female cast, I spot "Bernado," blue and white. Very picturesque, especially if somebody happens to be mending a net, however, apart from the actual fishing, which must contain an element of excitement, I have become increasingly aware of the dreary succession of tasks before and after this main event.

Before dawn they appear quietly out of the darkness, one with an outboard over his shoulder, the others lugging oars, nets, bait, buckets, and all manner of equipment needed for their trip. This group makes its way to one of the biggest boats and I see that it is Antonio and his three-man crew. Antonio is a large serious man who, unlike many of the others, goes out regularly and almost always returns with a good catch. He supplies some of the better restaurants where "Pescado de Barquillo" (Fish From the Small Boats) is one of the most expensive items on the menu.

His boat, "Maria," a sober green and white, is well kept and always left with a sturdy tarpaulin properly secured. There is little discussion. Each man seems to know exactly what is expected of him and goes about his work quietly and efficiently. Two of them untie the tarpaulin, pull it back, and fold it into a neat square.

After everything is carefully stowed, they get two additional helpers and, lining up on either side, strain to push the boat over a succession of wooden rollers to the water. Barefoot now, and with their pants rolled up, there is a final shove, the last man clambers aboard, the engine starts, and they are away, out through the break in the reef to the open sea.

Several hours after they have gone the sky darkens and the wind picks up. The sea becomes turbulent and before long, huge waves are smashing over the reef. It begins to rain, a driving, tropical downpour. This had been predicted and only Antonio went out this morning. Small groups of men gather in the shelter of the buildings and look anxiously out to sea, but just a few yards away, overcast clouds meet the water and not even the reef is visible. Now there are claps of thunder and jagged lightning.

Word goes out that Antonio's boat, attempting to return, has been swept past the opening in the reef to the seaward side of La Puntilla and is in danger of crashing onto the rocks. The coast guard sends a cutter to get a line to him, but after several failed attempts it also finds itself in difficulties.

Then, just as suddenly as it arrived, the storm begins to lose its force and the tide turns. Both Antonio's boat and the coast guard are able to make a new attempt at the passage. There are cheers and exclamations of relief as, pitching and rolling, they surge through into the relative calm of the lagoon.

I watch from my terrace as they arrive. There is still a strong wind but the sky has cleared and there is even a small knot of customers waiting—mostly middle-aged women in black with baskets or shopping bags, others just curious. A larger crowd of well-wishers gathers as the crew, aided by willing bystanders, hauls the boat up over the wet sand. There are hugs and back-slapping and some nervous laughter before Antonio, striving to look unmoved by his experience, uncovers the hatches to reveal mounds of fish shimmering in the sun. Since in any case I am planning to go for a walk and it has stopped raining, I decide to go down and take a closer look.

Outside my building on the Paseo there is the usual crowd of men—mostly fishermen that gather there each day, the ones Manuel complains about. As I thread my way through, I follow the custom of Spanish women and keep my eyes to myself so that few of them ever become familiar to me. One of the exceptions is "El Basco" who is there right now, engaged in a raucous argument—just as Manuel says. He is short, sturdy, and truculent, designed for combat and always looking for a fight. His deeply-lined mahogany face is decorated with its usual black stubble and he is drunk—I hope Manuel doesn't see this. Whether he is really Basque or not, he always wears a black beret, and wherever there is an uproar that sounds as though it is about to explode into physical violence, it is a safe bet that El Basco is at the center of it.

I go on down to the beach. Antonio has now switched from fisherman to salesman as he responds to requests for this or that fish, establishes what he considers a fair price, and firmly resists the bargain hunters. This is serious business, his sole reward for many hours of labor as well as hardships, such as the one he has just endured, so I suppose it is understandable that he should become pretty fed up with foreigners coming around asking unnecessary questions. Nevertheless, I notice some spectacular crimson fish among the catch and when he is weighing one I ask what they are called. No response.

"Fish?" I prompt after a few seconds. There is the faintest—the very *faintest*—flicker of a smile as he meets my eyes but he's not giving in so easily. I wait. Finally he replies.

"Señora, some people call them one thing. Others call them something else," and he goes on with his work. Thus dismissed, I return to the Paseo to continue my walk.

Coming toward me, fresh from his most recent debate, is El Basco. As we pass he glares at me. "So *you're* back!" he mutters, making me feel as welcome as a plague of locusts. This is obviously not *my* day.

He also has a boat—an unseaworthy looking little craft—but I have never seen him go out in it, which is probably just as well. Mostly he meets the fishing boats, waits until practically everything is sold, then puts in a bid for what's left. Almost immediately he is shouting and protesting but the fishermen are accustomed to this and eventually he stomps off with fish in two flat baskets suspended at either end of a wooden yoke balanced across his shoulders. He hawks them around the neighborhood and finally sets himself up at some street corner to sell the remainder. On my way back he is emerging from a restaurant shouting obscenities at the owner so I assume it's been no sale.

By the time I return, Antonio's catch has been disposed of, the crowd has dispersed, and he and his crew are cleaning up. With water from two pails that require endless trips to the sea to replenish, each removable part of the boat has been taken out, washed, scrubbed, set aside to drain, and then replaced. Now, all is in order, the tarpaulin has been made fast, and Antonio and his men head for home with their gear. As he comes up the ramp he turns toward me.

"Senora, that fish you asked about. It is called 'Sama'. Adiós."

* * * *

Another year has gone by and I am on my way back to Las Palmas. As I conjure up a mental picture of the beach and the surrounding area, it occurs to me that if I were to buy one of the modest fishermen's houses on La Puntilla and renovate it for myself, I would have one of the best locations on Las Canteras.

Apparently, the same thought, but on a grander scale, had already occurred to others. The morning after my arrival, I look out towards La Puntilla and I am horrified! The entire area where the fishermen's cottages stood has been razed. Heartsick, I walk over to inspect the situation.

The scene that confronts me is touching and melancholy. Two remaining houses cling precariously at the water's edge—rickety balconies lean toward the sea, a cloud of bougainvillea spills over a broken wall. Congregated on the rough, freshly-bulldozed earth, a group of fishermen are gathered around two chess players seated on boxes with a wooden crate for a table. Nearby, another group has collected some ruined chairs and sits chatting in the shade of a van. A companion works on a model ship. It is almost surrealistic, as though the streets and houses were still there in the background. I should like to ask about the circumstances that led to all this but remind myself that I am a foreigner and that such questions may be an intrusion.

Later, I see Manuel in the downstairs smorgasbord. After the usual greetings, I ask, "What has become of the fishermen?"

"They have been moved up the hill into completely new apartments, far superior to the places they previously occupied, many of which lacked even basic facilities. They are very fortunate."

"What will happen to La Puntilla?"

"A German consortium is negotiating for it. They have very big plans," he adds with obvious satisfaction. "A luxury hotel and condominiums."

"How marvelous! In no time at all Las Canteras will look exactly like Miami Beach." He looks puzzled as though he might be wondering what would be wrong with that?

I go out and make my way to the hill that he mentioned. It lies slightly to the north of the beach, faces south and is, in fact, a good location. Above the cliffs, apartment buildings of six or seven stories rise in orderly white blocks. They are light, airy, and well-spaced—and with about as much character as a computer print-out.

Nevertheless, as I walk by, I notice furtive splashes of color breaking the monotony. The wall of one terrace has been painted orange—probably against the rules—and here is a green door. Other apartments are painted around the windows—perhaps also inside—with colors reminiscent of La Puntilla. It is undoubtedly true that the new apartments are far superior to the dilapidated houses they left, but I sense the heartbreak as they abandoned the small rocky promontory that had been their universe. There, for generations, they had lived in their own way, apart from the others, wresting a living from the sea, and with the sound and the smell of the sea always at hand.

On my way back, I see, coming toward me, a person who closely re-sembles El Basco. As he draws closer, I realize with astonishment that it is indeed he, but an almost unrecognizable "he." First, he appears to be sober—an event in itself. His face is shaved and without the stubble only lightly tanned. He is wearing light grey, well creased pants and—of all things—an immaculate pale pink shirt! As we pass, he looks straight ahead, either to ignore my unwelcome presence or to discourage any reaction to his appear-ance. I never did discover what the occasion was—perhaps he was getting married—and never before or since has there been such a transformation.

As I return to the beach, I note with satisfaction that there seems to be no reduction in the number of boats drawn up. I am glad the fishermen are maintaining their foothold down here and that they show no sign of re-linquishing it. Actually, although each year an increasing number of tourists swarms into Las Palmas and settle over the beaches and surrounding area, there is little conflict. The fishing boats return with their catch in the morning, usually observed with great interest by the few tourists around at that hour, and by afternoon, the fish have been disposed of, boats have been pulled up, and the fishermen arrange themselves along the Paseo to observe with equal interest the sparsely-clad sunbathers sprawled on the beach below them.

When they tire of this, some will go off to one or another of the local bars and a few may get a little drunk. These days, most of the customers in bars and restaurants are foreigners—some of whom also tend to get a little drunk. But fishermen, in their knitted hats and serviceable sweaters who, among themselves, speak a brand of Spanish unintelligible to the rest, are becoming something of an embarrassment in an area that now considers itself rather chique. Sublimely unaware of this, even those who may have had one too many wobble out wishing those at hand a friendly but respect-ful "Adiós" and reel off happily into the night—perhaps even heading for La Puntilla before remembering that they now live in the brand-new apartments up the hill.

* * * *

It is fifteen years since the fishermen were moved from La Puntilla and their houses demolished. The land was cleared but the German consortium that was to have built a hotel and condominiums failed to materialize, and the area became an improvised parking lot. Then, just two years ago, the government, after many debates, finally decided it was just the place for a "cultural" center. Drilling through solid rock, workmen began excavating for foundations. Manuel was delighted. I, myself, could see no reason why every available space had to be built upon. I would have preferred a park but I made no comment.

"This," Manuel exclaimed, "will be wonderful for the community, and it will greatly increase the value of property in the area."

But, before actual construction could get under way, fate intervened on my side in the form of an election and a change of government. As a matter of principle, the new administration distanced itself from all policies of its predecessor. La Puntilla was found to be quite unsuitable for a cultural center. While alternatives were being considered, a car drove into one of the excavations so they were filled in. I was delighted. Manuel was so furious that he wrote a long, impassioned article which was published in the newspaper but to no effect.

In the meantime, the fishermen, although perhaps fewer in number, are still very much in evidence. Antonio, a little heavier now, continues to go out regularly and, just as regularly, returns with a good catch. El Basco's hair and even his stubble are grey and the black beret has been replaced with a red baseball cap so he doesn't look Basque any more. But he still meets the boats and waits to buy the last of the catch before going off on his rounds. There's a touch of the old fire from time to time—I came upon him the other day nose to nose with another vendor who had intruded upon his favorite street corner. But, on the whole, he is more subdued and even manages to tolerate my visits without signs of open hostility.

Suggestions are made from time tot time about how to convert La Puntilla, the most beautiful location on Las Canteras, from a disorganized and unsightly parking lot into something more appropriate, but so far no firm decision has been arrived at. The most recent suggestion was for a cultural center.

Encounters—The Canarios
Will Get You There

I am on my way to the telephone company to find out whatever became of one of their workmen. He came to install my telephone, fiddled around with some wires, and said he had to go downstairs to fetch some tools. That was two weeks ago and he hasn't been seen or heard from since. I interrupt two men chatting at the curb to ask directions.

"Si, Señora, the telephone company is just one block more—continue down to the corner," one tells me, pointing.

At the corner, however, three streets intersect and as I hesitate and search for a sign, a voice at my elbow says,

"Señora, it is over there, in the grey building." It is one of the men I had asked for directions and he had obviously been keeping an eye on me.

This is not unusual. When you ask a Canario how to get somewhere, he accepts total responsibility for seeing to it that you end up precisely where you are supposed to, even if he has to escort you there himself. And, in case you think this may be a gender thing, I ask a woman for directions and show her the address I am looking for.

"The building is just up there," she tells me. "Up the hill. The white one with the red door." I thank her but it is only a block away and I am early for my appointment so, to put in time, I walk very slowly and do a little window shopping. I soon become aware, however, that the woman to whom I had spoken is also dawdling and watching me furtively. She is probably wondering if I had correctly understood her directions and I realize that she won't be satisfied until she has me safely inside that red door. So, I prepare apologies for arriving ahead of time and, looking back as I enter, wave my thanks—thus releasing her from her burden of responsibility.

In the News—Crimes of Passion in the Test-tube

"Crimes of passion in the test-tube" is the title of an article on assisted procreation in this morning's paper. Among other things, it notes that sperm banks are having difficulty finding donors. In *this* country, it marvels, where men are supposed to be so *macho*! But of course, it observes, Spaniards may be macho but they are also practical. Sperm banks do not pay for this service, so a possible donor is likely to ask himself, *Why should I go to a sperm bank and masturbate for nothing when, also for nothing, I can do it more comfortably at home?*

Would he, himself, donate? Certainly not! For one thing, he does not believe in creating children anonymously—we are not breeding hamsters, he reminds us, and, in any case, he does not trust the assurance of confidentiality. He imagines himself, years hence, being accosted in the street by a teenager. "Hey, Papa! It's me—test-tube 6402!"

Valentina

Things have changed here in Las Palmas. Manuel has gone to the mainland and his wife, Valentina, is managing the apartments. She was already in charge when I came last year and everything seems to be going well. Before that, she was a shadowy figure that I had heard about but had never encountered. From various scraps of information, I gathered that she and Manuel had been separated for some years and, because the women I had seen him with from time to time had been extremely attractive but showy and overdressed, I expected something similar—and I was completely wrong. Attractive, yes, but forthright and down to earth. We liked one another immediately and soon became friends. Just the same I miss Manuel. His is a special personality and the place is not the same without him. Now, after another visit, I am about to return to New York.

On the morning of my departure I am up at five and surprised by a knock at the door. It is Valentina, with breakfast, which she has taken the trouble to get up and prepare for me.

The evening before, I had brought her a bouquet of flowers. I could hear her upstairs and called to her. She looked over the bannister.

"Julieta!" I cried dramatically, holding the flowers aloft. She had laughed and hurried down to receive them. She is setting the tray on a small table and checking to make sure everything is in order.

"Valentina, how kind of you. But you shouldn't have done this. It's too early."

"For me it is only a little earlier than usual," she responds cheerfully, "and I wanted to give you a good start on your journey." She wishes me a safe trip, we embrace, and she leaves. This will be the last time I will ever see her.

Over the following months we correspond intermittently. In one letter she asks if she can rent my apartment for herself until my return. I readily agree. There is another letter then silence. I write again. Several weeks later my letter is returned. Stamped on the envelope is the word "Fallecido"—deceased. I am shaken but not entirely convinced. I write to my lawyer who also happens to be hers. "Yes," he replies, "she died under tragic circumstances." I begin to wonder. If it had been illness or an accident, surely he would have said so. Then a mutual friend writes that she committed suicide. He does not describe the circumstances. I am incredulous, shocked, and finally, just terribly sad.

Over the ensuing weeks I think about her a great deal. Why did she do it? I sift through my recollections searching for clues but find none. She was good-humored, direct, and energetic. As likely to be found cleaning a hallway as closing a deal in the office.

"Valentina," I had said one day, "you work too hard. Can't you at least get somebody to do the cleaning for you?"

"I've tried," she replied "but nobody does it well enough to suit me. Besides, I enjoy physical labor. It keeps me in shape." And she certainly was in good shape. She had the light, springy step and the stance of a dancer—proud and challenging.

Whenever I think of her death I become frustrated. It doesn't fit. It is so completely out of character. There were no hang-ups, no fits of depression. She was all firmness and serenity. Had it really been a suicide?

A few months later, as I prepare for another visit to Las Palmas, I wonder how I will feel about the apartment knowing that Valentina might have died there. Will the torment and desperation that must have preceded such an act linger? Will the atmosphere still be charged with it? Had there been blood? Will there be stains or signs of stains having been removed? I resolve never to ask how or where she died and to discourage any discussion of the matter.

I unlock the door and let myself in. The apartment has been tightly closed. The air is warm and stale. In the gloom everything looks more or less as before. I pull back the heavy drapes and slide open the glass doors. There is a rush of cool air and suddenly the place is filled with sunlight. Happy sounds of children drift in from the beach. I step out onto the terrace, look across the bay, and breathe deeply.

I go back inside. I am still sad about Valentina's death but it no longer hovers over me. I don't search for ominous signs and they seem not to exist. I try to dismiss the whole matter from my thoughts. But unsolicited comments keep intruding. Manuel has returned and is now managing things.

"It is a complete mystery," he says. "There was absolutely no reason for it. She owed no money. Her accounts were in perfect order. There seemed to be no personal problems. As I am sure you know, we were separated. That was because some years ago, Valentina left me for another man." I am surprised— also skeptical. All very well, I think, for him to say that now she's not here to defend herself. To me, it seems more likely that it was he who was having an affair.

Then another. "She jumped from the terrace of the penthouse. In the morning they found her body on the Paseo. There was no explanation. Just a note saying she had decided to do it." Then it had been a suicide—but it had not happened in my apartment. I am relieved.

Still another. "It was when they owned the hotel that Valentina went off

66

to England with the manager. Teresa was only seven at that time. My wife took care of her." Teresa was her daughter.

So it *was* true. She *had* gone off with someone. Then, perhaps there had been another unhappy love affair. But this seems unlikely. Besides, in such a small community somebody would have known about it. I find myself puzzling more and more about her death, determined to find an explanation that seems beyond me. Finally, I give up.

* * * *

It is 1985. In today's paper there is an article about the divorce rate in Spain. It is said to be leveling off after the pent-up demand following legalization in 1981. 1981 was the year following Valentina's death and, for some reason, I keep thinking about it.

In 1980, it would already have been clear that very soon, divorce would become legal. Valentina had abandoned her husband and child and gone off with a lover. She had returned but, from that time, she and Manuel had lived separate lives. Obviously, there had been no true reconciliation. Soon, Manuel would be in a position to divorce her. He might even have stated his intention to do so.

Considering the circumstances, he would probably have little difficulty and no obligation to support her. Could she have been depressed about that? I dismiss the idea. Valentina was an extremely capable business woman, well able to take care of herself. The idea of being divorced should have held no great fear for her. On the contrary, I could rather imagine her enjoying the idea of this new phase of her life.

But what of their daughter? Teresa was then sixteen and studying abroad. She divided her vacations between Manuel and Valentina, both of whom adored her and each trying to be more lavish than the other. Valentina, anxious to make amends, perhaps, for having gone off and left her; Manuel attempting to make up for the years when he was too busy trying to make a success of his business to have time for his daughter.

Manuel had done well over the years and Teresa, their only child, would have been heir to a considerable fortune. But, suppose Manuel obtained a divorce? The situation might change. He could spend the money they had accumulated—perhaps on a new family. What would be left for Teresa? Thoughts such as these may have worried Valentina.

Furthermore, whatever her reasons for having left Manuel, Valentina must have felt considerable remorse at the trauma her sudden departure must have caused the seven-year-old Teresa. And now, in addition, this act of recklessness might indirectly deprive Teresa of her inheritance.

But there was a way out. Cruel but foolproof, provided one had the stomach for it. According to Spanish law, if one parent dies, half of the couple's assets must immediately be placed in trust for the children. The death of either Manuel or Valentina would assure their daughter's financial independence. Her own death could serve the purpose, but only if it occurred before the divorce.

I think about it more and more and, little by little, convince myself that I have found the answer. I can imagine Valentina, in her clear-headed fashion, weighing the pros and cons and arriving at the inevitable solution. A solution which would assure Teresa's financial security and, at the same time, demonstrate beyond any doubt, her love and concern for her daughter.

Is that what gave her the courage one night to go up to the penthouse, to step out onto the terrace, to climb over the rail, perhaps to pause for a moment, erect, challenging, and then, while the waves washed gently onto the beach, to let go? None of us would ever know for sure.

Shortly afterwards, during a conversation with Manuel, I find myself distracted and mulling it over again. He has said before that Valentina's death was a complete mystery to him. But was it? Had he not considered the same possibilities? Arrived at the same conclusions? As if he had read my thoughts, he leans toward me and his eyes narrow defiantly.

"When Valentina died," he says, slowly and deliberately, "I did not set aside half of my estate for Teresa as the law requires." He pauses, as if to observe my reaction, then continues dramatically, "I gave her *everything!*" He pauses again as if to let this sink in. "Stocks, bonds, real estate—it is all in her name." He continues. "If she told me tomorrow, 'Move from this building!' I should be obliged to do so."

So I was right.

Memories of the
Spanish Civil War

For various reasons it has been two years since I have been able to visit Las Palmas. My apartment is in the hands of an agent, but only a small portion of the annual rent has been deposited in my account. I have received no reply to several letters and I am concerned. Since at this time, it is impossible for me to go and look into the matter myself, I write to friends in Madrid and ask if the husband could fly down and see what is going on. He readily agrees and I supply the names and addresses of some of the people involved, one of whom is my lawyer. "But I know this man!" he writes back. "He is an old friend—we were in prison together during the Civil War."

I had forgotten that Nicolas had been imprisoned but his letter refreshes my memory. "We were in a concentration camp in 'La Isleta'," he explains. I am astonished! "La Isleta" is a peninsula that juts out just a few blocks from my apartment building. It is a military reservation, undeveloped except for army installations.

As it turns out, it was not my lawyer but my lawyer's father who had been his friend and, unfortunately, he has passed away in the meantime. Nevertheless, there are close ties and the problems concerning my apartment are speedily resolved, at least for the time being.

Meanwhile, Nicolas has been writing a book on the Civil War based in part on his own experiences. Shortly after his trip to the Canaries he sends me a copy. It describes the fact that when the war broke out he was a young lawyer in Grenada. Idealistic and concerned about injustices suffered by landless peasants at the hands of the local administration, he had become active in a campaign to help them. In the eyes of the newly installed Franco regime such conduct branded him as a communist and it was surprising that he was not immediately taken out and shot. Instead, he was imprisoned and sent to the Canaries.

All this I knew. What I had not realized was that when Nicolas used the term "concentration camp," he did so advisedly. As I read on, I begin to understand the extent of the mistreatment—the beatings, the torture—of how many prisoners died in captivity and how many others begged to die. I am forced to skip some passages because the details are too horrible.

Toward the end of the war, when conditions had become more humane, Nicolas speaks in the book of being part of a work crew assigned to clean up the beach. "The beach," it turns out was "Las Canteras"—*my* beach, the one that stretches out below my terrace! He describes the exhilaration, after almost three years captivity, of not only being outside the camp but of being able to look out across the sea and visualize the world that, at times, he had almost given up hope of ever seeing again. He had even heard rumors that the war was coming to an end and that political prisoners might soon be released. By the time the conflict was over, however, mistreatment had caught up with him and he was shipped back to the mainland in a coma. When he finally regained consciousness, he was astonished to find himself in a hospital in Madrid with his mother at his bedside.

Realizing what he had gone through, I am overcome with remorse at having asked him to return to the scene of such a dark chapter in his life—and amazed that he had agreed to go. But when I express my regrets, Nicolas, the happiest of individuals and an eternal optimist, says no, he has put all that behind him and was delighted at the opportunity to return under such pleasant circumstances.

And, when I, myself, go back to Las Palmas I find that his experiences have added a new dimension to the surrounding area. As I think of Nicolas, the kindest and gentlest of men, and the terms of his confinement, the bleak hills of La Isleta, rising beyond the benign tourist sprawl of hotels and apartment buildings, have become darkly sinister. The beach, on the other hand, where he labored under the watchful eyes of prison guards and which I have always enjoyed tremendously, is now almost hallowed ground, while the view out to sea, which must have meant so much to him, sparkles in a way that it never did before. I sense the unquenchable optimism as he revelled in that brief moment of freedom, and dreamed of the day when the nightmare would be over and he could start living again. And live, he has, overcoming years of exile and adversity with a zest and enthusiasm which, I suspect, only those who have emerged from the shadow of death are fully able to achieve.

A Morning at the Beach

At this time of the year, daybreak is late and it is around seven before one can discern the faint outline of fishing boats drawn up on the sand and shadowy figures moving silently among them. Suddenly the quiet is interrupted by the giggles and breathless squeals of a group of elderly bathers taking their early morning dip. In half an hour they are gone, leaving the beach deserted again except for the fishermen and a few expectant gulls.

Soon the sun is up and the water looks inviting. The waves sweeping in from the open sea dash themselves to pieces on a reef about a quarter of a mile off shore, leaving an extensive lagoon of relatively calm water, clear enough even when one is swimming some distance out, to see a solid bottom of clean, rippled sand.

I decide to have my swim before the crowd arrives. Apart from a young boy practicing with his scuba gear in the shallows, I am the only one in the water. Then even he goes ashore. It is pleasantly cool and I begin to count my strokes. The aim is to go a little further each day—one day I may find myself in Morocco, seventy miles due east, you can't miss it, except I realize later I was headed due west—first stop, Miami Beach.

In any case, I reflect, I don't really care too much about swimming entirely by myself. Mostly I swim on my back so I don't always see what's ahead. Suppose I bumped into somebody and started to say "Oh, I'm terribly sorry," and it turned out to be a large fish—a shark, for example. Manuel assures me that he has studied the matter and that sharks would never venture into the shallow water inside the reef—he says they're too smart for that. However, this theory assumes all sharks to have similar IQs—which may or may not be the case. What about the slightly-retarded character who may come wandering in simply because he doesn't know any better? Or the one that, although as smart as the rest, is just up to here with sea food?

God! What's that long dark shadow I see out of the corner of my eye! I swivel and it does too! I open my mouth to scream then realize that it is my own long, dark shadow on the bottom. Why am I such a coward?

Manuel likes to swim at low tide and if low tide happens to be at ten or eleven at night that's when he plunges in, splashing and gurgling as he switches from breast stroke to crawl to butterfly all the way across the bay and back. I personally consider this quite foolhardy. Apart from the odd denizen of the deep one may encounter out there in the dark, Manuel has suffered two serious heart attacks, but this doesn't deter him and he appears to enjoy it immensely. I envy his courage.

I emerge safe and sound after my own frightening encounter with my shadow, but need to dry off so I make my way to Felipe, one of the concessionaires who rents out sun lounges. Felipe is large and capable, a good deal taller than most Spaniards, and he keeps a protective eye on the flock that settles around his cabaña. As I approach he is fixing a cold inhospitable stare on an idler who seems to have no particular business in the area.

His clients are mostly Swedes and Germans and he knows enough of their language to do business with them. They, on the other hand, are almost as reluctant to learn a foreign language as the English. "Say it loud," they argue "and they'll understand." Yet Spaniards make it very easy for foreigners, praising and encouraging even the most halting attempt to speak their language.

Felipe never fails to make a big thing of my own limited ability in this respect. For the benefit of those within earshot he holds long and unnecessary conversations with me in Spanish. "Where would you like to sit, Señora?" "Is this a suitable place?" "Would you like to face the sea or be with your back to the sun?" "We are fortunate to have such a beautiful day, are we not?" And when he is through, even though my end of the conversation has consisted of monosyllables, he never fails to announce to the beach population at large "Here is a foreigner who speaks our language very correctly," making it abundantly clear if this specimen which he has on display can do it, anybody can.

In fact, most of his audience are not interested in speaking his language or any other and, at the moment, they resemble nothing more than a collection of dead bodies. They are here for one purpose—the sun. Swedes especially have a deep sense of deprivation in this respect. They appear around eleven, smother themselves with sunblock, settle themselves on their cots and lapse into a state of blissful semi-consciousness from which they arouse themselves at intervals to turn over. They snap out of it around four, gather their things together and head for home, well satisfied with their day.

I am soon stretched out along with them, nicely relaxed after my swim. But the beach is beginning to fill up and soon the vendors arrive. First, announcing his wares in Swedish, German, and Spanish and at the top of his lungs, comes Paco, the ice cream man, a well-known character around here, although a little subdued this morning. Then comes "café," also in a fine voice. He is followed by "Perros calientes" (hot dogs) and then the more traditional "Pan y huevos" (bread and eggs) and, to wash all this down, "beer,

Coca-Cola, and Seven-Up." But how can one pass a day at the beach without knowing what's going on in the world, so a newsboy joins the chorus.

As the demand for ice cream picks up, Paco seems to have cast off his gloom and is becoming his jolly old self. In fact, it becomes increasingly clear, that at least some of the profits are being invested at one of the local bars. The litany of ice cream flavors acquires a certain rhythm and is injected here and there with a sly observation concerning the sunbathers as he sambas his way among the cots. "Gracias, Abuela" (Thanks, Grandmother) he remarks cheerfully to an unsuspecting lady half his age. Where he thinks he can get away with it he tweaks a toe or pats a shoulder. Since I am in no mood to be tweaked or patted I studiously avoid even looking at him.

Now he is waiting to serve an elderly woman who is helping her infirm husband get settled. "One chocolate, one vanilla—and two for the sanatorium" he chants impudently, but in Spanish of course. Those of us who understand ignore him and Felipe, who has been observing his performance with growing disapproval, mutters impatiently. Offended, and now a little drunk, he becomes defiant and when a frail but kindly old gentleman raises his skinny frame to beckon him over, he approaches singing merrily "and this one for the crematorium." The old man, unaware that he is being ridiculed, smiles indulgently and hands him a tip which Paco shamelessly pockets. Felipe, now openly disgusted waves him away with an angry "Basta (Enough)! Get out of here and don't come back!"

At this point I decide that I have enjoyed the best of the day so I pick up my towel and head for home. As I leave the beach, I feel a little sorry for Paco trudging along beside me, exiled and subdued. Then he spies a shapely young woman approaching and his mood changes instantly.

"Hola! Vitamina!" he warbles twisting his hips invitingly.

In the News—
The British Royals

In Las Palmas, treatment of the news can be lighthearted and irreverent. A government program that has been reduced in scope is said to have been "decaffeinated" and an article concerning sewage at the beaches—a potentially devastating situation where tourism is the principal industry—is headed "All of the ocean is not orégano."

News of the British Royals is of special interest. Today, an article refers to "The Queen Mother" with no further identification, as though there is only one queen mother in the whole world and everybody knows who she is. In Spain, she is obviously held in very high esteem.

The piece describes the scene outside her home as a crowd gathers in the morning to wish her well on her ninety-fourth birthday. They brought gifts, states the writer, including a bottle of gin which, it is said, she rather enjoys. She is as "fresh as a breeze from the ocean" and "as beautiful as a geranium" (Geraniums are one of the favorite flowers in the Canaries).

Prince Charles does not come off nearly as well. A paragraph covering a visit to Spain by Charles and Diana raves over the Princess—beautiful, charming, gracious, etc. "As for Charles—poor fellow looked as though he'd just given blood to the Red Cross."

Returning After an Absence

It is my first visit to Las Palmas in three years and it has started out badly. My overnight flight from New York was late arriving in Madrid, so I missed my connection and, not surprisingly, when I eventually arrived in Las Palmas my suitcase was not to be found. Having had no sleep to speak of for the past twenty-four hours, I am not in the best of humors as I arrive at Casa Manuel. My key does not fit the front door—the lock must have been changed, perhaps there has been a robbery.

Cristo, the owner of a boutique on the first floor comes out and greets me.

"I will call Manuel," he says.

"Manuel is back!"

"Yes, he returned a month ago but he no longer lives in the penthouse," and he pushes another bell. "There is a lady here to see you," he announces. Then, turning to me, "He will be down in a few minutes. Please come in and sit down."

I am delighted that he is back and when he appears I am astonished at the change in him. He looks ten years younger.

"You look marvelous!" I exclaim as he pulls up a chair.

"I feel marvelous," he responds cheerfully. "And my health has never been better. It took two heart attacks to achieve this transformation. You have come to spend some time here?"

"Yes. I expected that Fernando might be here. He has been taking care of my apartment."

"I believe your apartment is occupied."

"Occupied!" I am dismayed. "But I arranged that it would be available."

"Perhaps I am wrong then. I will call him." Then, "He is coming. He will be here shortly."

"You are back for good?" I ask.

"I am not sure. I have business to attend to and then I will decide. I have to do something about the restaurants. They are now closed."

"I thought your cousin was looking after them for you."

"He was—the son-of-a-bitch. But I will tell you about that some other time."

Then Fernando arrives. We have not met before. He is a slight man of about forty and he seems agitated—not surprising since he owes me several thousand dollars.

"Your apartment is occupied at present," he says, "but I also take care of the one above and that one is available."

"But how come my apartment is occupied?" I ask coldly. "My lawyer advised you that I would be here on the twenty-seventh," and I produce a copy of his letter. "I also wrote directly to you," and I produce a copy of that letter. Fernando looks uncomfortable.

"The lawyer said you might be coming but he was vague," he retorts impatiently, "and I never received a letter from you."

"There is a letter for you in the mail rack," Manuel interjects and he goes out and returns with it. It is my letter still unopened.

There is a moment's embarrassment before Fernando pulls himself together and replies airily, "Well, there is really no problem. As I said, the apartment above is exactly the same as yours." I could feel my temper rising.

"Señor, I made this trip to spend some time in my own apartment and I made the necessary arrangements. I have no intention of staying in somebody else's."

"But it is occupied," he shrugs helplessly. "The tenants will not want to move and, as I told you, the other one is exactly the same."

"Then move the people out of my apartment into the one that is *exactly the same*," I snap, my voice rising. "And, if they do not want to move, explain that you have made a foolish mistake and *insist*." He stubs out his cigarette and lights another. I say nothing. Finally he gets to his feet and disappears. When he returns he looks distressed.

"They say they have a contract and refuse to move. It will only be for a week," he pleads.

"Actually," says Manuel, "it would be easier for *you* to move since you have no luggage." Why doesn't he mind his own business, I think irritably. Fernando looks close to tears.

"Very well," I concede reluctantly. "Let us leave it as it is for the time being."

That evening, as I am preparing for bed, there is a ring at my door. I assume it is Iberia Airlines with my suitcase and put on my raincoat to answer it. Not so—it is Manuel.

"I wondered if you would have dinner with me," he says.

"I should love to, Manuel, but could we make it tomorrow? I feel as though I haven't slept for a week—also I have just laundered my underwear." Nevertheless, I am pleased at the invitation and even more pleased when he calls the next day, eager to confirm it.

The fact that Manuel is back makes everything seem more like old times—how fortunate that his return coincided so well with my own. It is also fortunate that Iberia showed up this morning with my suitcase and that I will have something decent to wear.

As usual, he appears exactly on time. These days he has become very naval in appearance. In marked contrast to his "Western period," he is wearing a navy cap with gold braid, a white safari jacket, and dark pants. As we walk along the Paseo, I am surprised when two young men salute him—and even more surprised when he snaps one back. He smiles happily.

"They are probably seamen," he explains, "and the braid on this cap suggests that I am a captain in the merchant marine. That is why they saluted." I wonder why he would wear a cap that is so misleading but before I can comment, he continues. "Actually it is a little ridiculous because the moment I set foot on a boat I become violently ill. In fact, several years ago I had an unfortunate experience because of that. I met a German girl, a beautiful blond, and I was doing everything to please her. Then she suggested going to Tenerife on the hydrofoil and I was dismayed. However, as a precaution, I took a massive dose of Dramamine before leaving."

"And did it work?"

"It was a *disaster*. I slept all the way over and when we arrived she was unable to wake me. Everybody assumed I was either drunk or on drugs. We flew back in complete silence and I never saw her again."

"Oh, Manuel! What a shame! Couldn't you have explained?" Actually I remember seeing them together and I didn't think she was so special.

"So, tell me," I say, after we are seated and have toasted one another, "where have you been all this time? When last I heard you were in Madrid."

"Yes, but when Valentina died there were many things to attend to here so I returned. After a year I went to Mexico where I managed a ranch for a friend during his absence. Then I travelled in South America and spend some time in Chile—also on a ranch. That is the life I really prefer but first I must do something about the restaurants."

"Are you thinking of reopening them?"

"Not on my own—I would end up having another heart attack. But if my daughter were interested I could help her get established. On the other hand, I feel she is better off in California—it is a good life there. She will come for a visit, then we will decide."

"That was an unfortunate mix-up about your apartment," he says after a pause. "And by the way, I had not realized you have such a bad temper."

"You mean my set-to with Fernando?" He nods. "Actually that was not my *bad* temper. That was only my *medium* temper."

"Dios mio!" he murmurs, crossing himself. "For myself I try not to get too excited about things. It was when Valentina and I separated that I had my first heart attack. Then, if I died, I knew she would inherit half of my estate—it is the law—and at that time there was no divorce in this country. So I put everything in the name of my brother and gave him a power of attorney. It remained that way for several years. Then after her death I asked for the assets to be transferred back. My brother refused unless I paid him an extremely large sum of money. That was when I had my second heart attack.

"The money was supposed to be for taking care of everything—I believe it was his wife's idea. Finally I had to do this. It was also at that time I discovered my cousin had been cheating me with the restaurants. That was a big disappointment. I had brought him from Córdoba when he had nothing—also my brother for that matter—and both had double-crossed me—son-of- bitches."

"Sons-of-bitches," I correctly gently.

"Yes, yes—sons-of-bitches—thank you. In business," he continues, "one has to be very careful when dealing with friends or relatives. With strangers, one demands a clear understanding of all aspects of a transaction, while with friends or relatives one tends to become careless about such details, and this can lead to serious misunderstandings. Also, in business, your friend may not want to take advantage of you but, conditioned by a life-time of not only succeeding but surviving by his wits, it is second nature for him to try for the best deal. He feels compelled to do this." Am I being warned that when it comes to business between us I am on my own?

"But in spite of everything," I tell him, "you look extremely well. You've put on some weight and it suits you." He smiles broadly.

"That, of course, depends upon the point of view. In any event, I have never felt better. I did a great deal of study about the heart and the way it functions. Then I embarked on a program through diet and exercise to repair the damage that had been done and to improve my health. It has worked extremely well.

"I no longer smoke, I drink very little, I walk the length of the Paseo and back three times a day—a little over twelve kilometers; that is in connection with my metabolism—plus I swim one kilometer. I am very strong and my heart is in perfect condition."

"How fortunate, Manuel, that you have such a positive attitude about these things and that you set out to understand them. I don't even want to know how my body functions. I would be afraid of becoming a hypochondriac. Was it difficult to give up smoking?"

"Yes, it was quite difficult. As you may recall, I was never without a cigarette. But I knew I had to do it. I am also very careful about my diet—fruit for breakfast and a special porridge made with several grains. Salads, a little chicken, fresh vegetables. I have also invented a drink with the blender of papaya, milk and honey—it is delicious. You must try it. I now do my own cooking. When I remarry I will probably cook for two."

As one who hates to cook, that last remark really catches my interest.

"By the way," he continues after a pause, "I understand you may be interested in selling your apartment."

"It is a possibility. But that's one reason I am here—to decide whether to sell it, rent it, or maybe even occupy it myself."

"If you should decide to sell, I may be interested in buying it."

"But don't you own the one you are presently occupying?"

"That is true, but in case my daughter should return I would want another for her. Now would be an excellent time for you to sell. You could invest the money for a very good return."

"I suppose I could, but I enjoy the apartment and if I continue to come to Las Palmas I would have to rent—maybe something not as nice."

"Well, but if one rents, one has no responsibility for upkeep. After almost twenty years the plumbing in the building is beginning to deteriorate. I know for a fact that some of the pipes will have to be replaced shortly. It will be difficult for you to find reliable people to attend to these matters. You could save yourself a lot of problems."

"I would have to think about it. For one thing, since I have been away for some time, I am not sure how much the apartment is worth."

"I would be willing to give you a good price, in cash, some of it in U.S. dollars. By the way, there is an Englishman, a guest of the owner of apartment 401. I understand he is also interested in buying an apartment in the building. He will probably come to see you. I would be very careful. I have heard some adverse comments about him."

"Well, thank you. I'm glad you mentioned it and if I do decide to sell I would certainly prefer to deal with you. However, I need a little time to decide about my plans," I respond. Privately, I am disappointed. I had begun to think Manuel might be madly in love with me—an intriguing idea—but now I see it is my apartment that is the big attraction and his haste to arrange a date was probably motivated by the need to get his bid in ahead of that Englishman—a possible rival in this connection.

The following morning, I am gazing idly out at the Paseo when I see Manuel setting out at a brisk pace, his ever-present cap at its usual jaunty angle. Yesterday, he didn't remove it even for lunch—since we were outdoors, it was not inappropriate but I wonder if he might not be losing some hair.

Then, in one of those seemingly inexplicable episodes of ESP that occurs from time to time, he seems to become aware of my presence for he stops, does an about-face and looks up at my terrace. He sees me, turns abruptly and pushes his way hurriedly through the crowd as though angry at himself for having been caught in the act.

Renovation—and Then Some!

Now that I have decided to keep my apartment for my own use, I am suddenly dissatisfied with its appearance. What seemed okay when I had tenants doesn't look so good anymore. Previously, I hadn't noticed that the wallpaper is soiled in places and beginning to peel; or that the carpet in the living room has worn patches, and it didn't seem important that, somehow or other, during the several years I was absent, a Swedish-style couch and two chairs disappeared and were replaced by vinyl non-Swedish impostors. There's nothing for it but to renovate.

Manuel recommends a decorator who has worked for him over the years—in fact he did the original interiors of this very building. Umberto is a bright, intelligent man armed with a computer and in short order he is able to multiply, divide, tot everything up, and tell me what each aspect of the work will cost. Since he speaks no English and my Spanish is unreliable when it comes to numbers, I hand him a pen and paper and ask him to put the estimates in writing. He looks uncomfortable—perhaps he thinks I am questioning his honesty. But as he prints out the words, slowly and laboriously, I realize that, although extremely efficient with the computer, he is barely literate without it.

He explains that, at the moment, he is busy on another job that he has promised to finish and I explain that my work has to be completed before I leave in ten days.

"We will start immediately," he says, with the duplicity of an experienced contractor, and could I go with him tomorrow to select the carpeting?

In the morning he arrives with an assistant and we drive to an area of carpet dealers. He parks the car and we get out, but instead of going to one of the stores we head for the nearest bar. In Spain, bars normally serve coffee and snacks as well as alcohol but when Umberto says "Would you care for a drink, Señora?" I suspect he doesn't mean coffee. It's only 10:30 so I pass.

"Coffee, then?" I accept. Each of them orders a double scotch—name brands, the best—which they polish off before I have even finished my demi-tasse. Having ordered the carpeting, we return to the apartment and prepare for the big push. I remove all small items from the furniture and put books, ornaments and even a vase of flowers into one of the closets. Then as they begin to move the furniture, I decide this would be an excellent time to vacate the place and head for the Paseo.

In Spain, the workday normally extends from 8:00 A.M. until 1:00 P.M. and from 3:00 P.M. until 6:00 P.M. When I return after six, they have finished stripping the paper and have prepared the walls for plastering. A shrouded pyramid of furniture stands in the middle of the living room and another in the bedroom. There are cans of paint, bags of plaster, ladders, and all manner of tools and equipment all over the place. A thick coating of white covers the sink and the kitchen counters. I am obliged to go out for dinner. Later, I realize there is no sign of my bed and when I discover that it is holding up the pyramid of furniture in the bedroom I begin to wonder if this whole thing was really necessary. Perhaps what was good enough for my tenants should have been good enough for me.

The following day I am in the apartment when the crew returns for the afternoon shift. One of the workmen asks if I have a bottle.

"A bottle of what?" I ask.

"He wants an *empty* bottle," one of the others explains patiently, "to mix whiskey and water." In an hour or so, the crew, who had returned smelling of liquor but reasonably sober, are in a state of alcoholic euphoria. This crowd makes the three-martini lunch look like a dowagers' afternoon tea party. Finally their level of intoxication makes me uneasy. For example, out on the terrace, one of them is up a ladder far above the railing and he is swaying noticeably as he paints the ceiling. Realizing that disaster is just a misstep away, and being a coward at heart, I leave for the afternoon.

The next day I return from an errand to find a perfect stranger padding about in his bare feet. Stripped to the waist and clad in a pair of jeans, he looks so at home that I wonder for a moment if I am in the wrong apartment. No, we are both in the right place. He's the plasterer, good looking in a John Wayne sort of way with well-developed muscles all over the place, but I resent his bold speculative stare and I am glad that Umberto and his men are around. In any event, he works quickly and in two days he is gone.

The work is going well, but as Umberto is about to paint the bathroom, he draws my attention to a damp spot on the ceiling which for some time I have been determined not to notice.

"I believe it is a leak," he says. "We should have the plumber look at it." Pepe comes and declares that it is indeed a leak.

"We will have to open it up," he says. I picture him slicing out a section with some sharp instrument, but what he goes up the ladder with is a large, unscientific mallet. To my horror, he lets fly at the ceiling, showering himself and everything else with debris, but achieving the desired result—a large hole, albeit a jagged one.

"It is a question of age," he observes as he replaces a corroded pipe.

"But the pipes up there are all the same age," I point out. "Before long the others will also have to be replaced."

"You are right," he responds gravely. "Plumbers have to make a living, Señora."

The work has been going on for three days and I have been getting up earlier than usual so as to have the breakfast things out of the way by the time the workmen arrive. This morning, eight o'clock comes and goes and there is no sign of them. The silence is eerie. I suspect that, like a man trying to please two mistresses, Umberto has gone back to his other job for awhile. Finally the telephone rings. It is Umberto and he has terrible news: Yesterday evening his eighteen-year-old son was struck and killed by a drunken driver. Haltingly, I express my sympathy as best I can. After two days they return. Everybody is subdued and Umberto is gaunt and red-eyed. He shows me a photo of a handsome young man with a pleasant smile and a strong resemblance to himself. I cannot begin to imagine his grief.

Later, I ask Manuel if he has heard about the accident. Yes, he says, he has. He sounds matter of fact and I am surprised.

"Umberto and his wife must be distraught," I venture.

"Distraught! They're not distraught," he scoffs. "He was *retarded!*" I am stunned for a moment. Then indignant and angry.

"Would they have loved him less because of that?"

"No, no, of course not," he responds, hastily changing his tone and looking embarrassed. "It was a terrible thing to happen. Yes, they must be very upset."

In the photograph that Umberto had shown me there was no sign that the boy was not completely normal. In fact, it turns out that he had been only slightly retarded. Nevertheless, Manuel's initial reaction was something that I would never completely forget.

Taking into account the two-day interruption, Umberto estimates that everything will be finished by the weekend, but by Friday it is clear that he has been over-optimistic and although I try not to show it, I am deeply disappointed. I have been counting the hours when I would be free of the chaos in which I have been living.

Aware of my feelings and, in spite of his grief, Umberto is contrite that he was not able to keep his promise. He sets about creating a personal environment to see me through the weekend. He clears a space in the living room, extricates a chair and a small table from under the canvas covers, dusts them off and places them just so, then fishes out the flowers that I had put in the closet several days ago and sets them on the table. Satisfied with the general effect, he gestures grandly for me to take a seat and heads for the door. Then, he glances back and, with an expression of mock exasperation, returns to pick up a flower petal that had dropped to the table and pop it into the vase. Obviously delighted with himself at this last fastidious touch, he wishes me a pleasant weekend and leaves.

Everything is finally completed the day before I am to return to New York. Umberto has done a beautiful job and under very difficult circumstances. He has hinted that it might be nice if we could have a small fiesta when the work is finished, so I am ready with a variety of snacks and, of course, liquor. We all toast the work and one another and, in my own state of euphoria, I give one of the workmen the vinyl-covered couch and chairs which, with the help of the others, he loads immediately into his station wagon, before I can sober up sufficiently to change my mind.

Then, as a final act, I very carefully write out Umberto's check and have him verify that it is in order. I have given the workmen their tips and added something to the check for himself. He is well pleased, we express our deep respect and lasting admiration for each other, and he goes off happily wishing me a safe journey.

First thing in the morning, when I return from picking up my breakfast rolls, I am surprised to see him standing outside my building. I assume he must be doing a job for somebody else. But he looks reproachful as he greets me and he has my check in his hand. In Spanish, the word for "thousand" is "mil"—an insignificant little word. So insignificant, in fact, that in making out the check, I had somehow failed to include it. The result is instead of having a check for eighty thousand pesetas (around eight hundred dollars) he has one for eighty pesetas—less than a dollar. I am appalled at my carelessness but feel compelled to remind him that he approved the check when I wrote it. Of course, we had been drinking from the same cup, so to speak, which may explain the dual oversight.

I don't believe he thinks for a moment that I deliberately tried to cheat him but the experience has obviously left him quite shaken—and I don't blame him. After all, he had worked hard and had his men to pay, I was about to fly off to New York, and there he was with a check for eighty cents. No wonder he is in a state of shock. I make out a new check. He examines this one meticulously, word by word, numeral by numeral. Watching him leave, I suspect he is making a bee-line for the bank to cash it before I flee the country—just in case. I would do exactly the same.

Friday Surprise

I am exuberantly cheerful as I leave Pauline's apartment. Yesterday I arrived from New York just in time for the weekly meeting of the "Friday Group," a clutch of kindred spirits who gather each Friday at noon for drinks and tapas and whatever bits of news may have surfaced during the week. The tapas had been excellent, the drinks as stimulating as usual and, after an absence of several months I had been reunited with old friends. I am within walking distance of my apartment but wait with several of our group who need a taxi.

Suddenly, one of them cries "Look out!" and I feel a hand sliding the straps of my handbag over my shoulder. I grab them as a young man slips them down my arm.

"Go away!" I shout as I pull the bag toward me. But he has a good grip on it. In a flash we are toe to toe, tugging for all we are worth. Then one of the straps breaks—shoddy material. "Go away!" I shout again, still hanging on to the remaining strap. He gives the bag another jerk and I am left with nothing but the strap in my hand. It has parted company from the bag—shoddy workmanship.

He runs. And I, unable to accept the loss of my handbag, set off in pursuit. A woman joins me, warning "No, no, Señora!" Then the owner of a café at the scene dashes out, grabs the cane from one of my companions, leaving her to totter about as best she can, and joins the chase. At that moment, Richard, another member of our group, emerges from Pauline's building, sees me streaking by and not having the slightest idea who or what I am pursuing, races after me.

Looking back, it seems that all this would have made a wonderful frieze in the style of ancient Greece. I could see us tearing along, one behind the other in a beautifully carved panel above the entrance to the Acropolis—the robber, myself, the Spanish woman, the café owner brandishing the walking stick, followed by Richard with a few curious townspeople bringing up the rear.

Anyway, back to the chase. I am not doing badly at this point. I am reasonably fleet of foot and, as we approach a corner, I have the inside track on the sidewalk while my assailant, who is in the street, has to run around some parked cars. We haven't counted on an accomplice, however. He is sitting on a motorcycle all revved up for the getaway. Our quarry leaps aboard and away they speed.

Since my keys are in the bag, I decide to pick up another set from María, who cleans for me, and go home immediately in case they decide to rob my apartment. Once home, I call the local police to report the matter and I am told that I must appear in person, so down I go.

As I wait my turn in the lobby, feeling shaken now that the excitement of the chase is over and quite dejected, I look out and there, silhouetted against the light in his familiar yachting cap, is Manuel. What a welcome sight! He looks concerned but his voice is studiously matter of fact as he announces,

"Your bag has been found."

"But how did you know I had been robbed? And how did you know I was here?" I ask in amazement.

"The robber threw your bag away and it was picked up by a Señor Ortega who lives at the other end of the Paseo. He found your name and telephone number in your address book but you were not home. Then he looked through your book for somebody in the same building and he found me."

"How nice of him to go to so much trouble."

"Yes, and very intelligent. As for knowing where you were," he added, "I simply used my head. Having been robbed where would you be? At the police station, naturally. Come, I will go with you to the apartment of Señor Ortega."

Needless to say, there is no money in the bag when I recover it, but my keys are there and, of course my address book, for which I am truly grateful—I have since made a copy.

As we walk back along the Paseo, I sort out my losses—around two hundred dollars in cash and two pairs of glasses. On the plus side, I had been carrying no important papers and no credit cards and—perhaps most important of all—I had not been injured. Helen Buckley, a nurse at the International Clinic, had had her bag wrenched off with such force that she was thrown backwards and suffered a fractured pelvis. By comparison, my robber had behaved quite nicely. There had been determination during our tug of war, but no real malice and, I reflect, with the unemployment level in his age group around 50 percent, who knows what lay behind this act of banditry.

"Manuel, I am very tired," I complain, lagging behind him and hoping he will suggest we take a cab—since I have no money I don't feel that I can be the one to suggest it.

"I am also tired," he responds curtly, not even slowing his pace.

Typically, Manuel does something for me voluntarily and with obvious pleasure, then suddenly, in the course of events, becomes cranky as though he might be angry with himself for having become involved. Well, we are more than half way.

Actually, the glasses were a greater loss than the money. Too bad I hadn't had Ida's robber. Her robber was a woman and as she raced off with Ida's bag, Ida, who is lost without her reading glasses, screamed after her in a panic, "My glasses! My glasses!" Without breaking stride, the obliging robber fumbled around, found the glasses, and jettisoned them. Quite gallant, I thought.

"What should I do for Señor Ortega?" I ask as we get closer to home.

"I'm sure he doesn't expect anything but, if you want to, perhaps you could send some flowers to his wife."

"Good idea." Then, as we arrive at my apartment, "Thank you for everything, Manuel. You have been very kind and extremely helpful."

"Not at all. I am glad that I could be of assistance."

"And, Manuel," I add, teasing, "perhaps I could send *you* some flowers?"

"No, you could *not* send me some flowers," he relies stiffly and stalks off.

Encounters—
At the Post Office,
Carnations for the Ladies

At the Post Office: Canarios are indulgent toward foreigners. I can imagine their saying "Poor things. They mean well but they're not too bright." So they seem to feel an obligation to protect us whenever the need arises.

I am waiting in line at the post office to buy stamps for some postcards. I happen to have three of them in my hand.

"Stamps for thirteen postcards to the United States," I say in Spanish when my turn comes. The woman behind me leans in front of me and speaks directly to the clerk.

"She means to say *three*," she tells him with complete authority. The clerk looks back at me.

"For how many cards, Señora?"

"Thirteen," I reply firmly.

"But," insists the woman, addressing the clerk again as though I do not exist, "she has them in her hand and she *has only three.*"

Finally, I have to interject. I thank her for helping me, but explain that I have ten other cards at home. She subsides, crestfallen, obviously disappointed at having missed an opportunity to be of service.

Carnations for the Ladies: My taxi enters the wrought iron gates of the Hotel Santa Catalina, follows the curved driveway through the lush green of its well-cultivated gardens, and deposits me at the main entrance. The tall columns of its facade, fronted by towering palms, remind me of the "Royal Hawaiian," but here dark wood balconies against clean white stucco are unmistakenly Spanish. A gracious establishment of a past era, although the scene in the lobby is very much of the present—a crowd of tourists in dripdries and sensible shoes, festooned with cameras and clutching bottles of mineral water, milling around before being herded off on a sight-seeing tour.

In the dining room, however, all is grace and serenity. I lunch with three women friends to the delightful accompaniment of live Chopin in a charming setting with impeccable service. With my paella I order a bottle of the local beer. A waiter at my elbow displays the label for my approval.

An elderly, very well-turned out, and eminently respectable-looking Swedish couple enter. The husband is extremely drunk, but in a most regal and proper fashion. Under the watchful eye of the maitre d' he seats himself with exquisite care, and beseeches him to feed them immediately for they are faint with hunger.

We are about to have dessert when the husband of one of my friends comes in to speak with her. He apologizes for intruding and presents each of us with a pink carnation which he has procured en route.

Marta

Now that I plan to spend more time in Las Palmas, I will no longer rent out the apartment, so instead of an agent, I will need somebody just to clean for me and keep an eye on it when I am away.

From time to time I have encountered Marta mopping the stairs or the hallways or swilling what was left in the bucket over the pavement out front. She is heavy, slow moving, and always in black but industrious and pleasant enough, and she has been employed by Manuel for some years.

"Marta," I ask one day, "would you have time to clean my apartment for me?"

"Of course, Señora, I would be glad to do it. Besides, I am very poor and I need the money. I have worked for the Señor in 701 for three years. He will give you a good reference—otherwise he is extremely tight."

She comes and looks the situation over. "There is much to be done," she observes disapprovingly. "It is obvious that this apartment has been seriously neglected." Then, she examines the contents of my utility cupboard. "You will need a vacuum cleaner," she informs me, "and not a cheap one like that of the señor on the fifth floor which is completely useless." She enumerates other items that I should provide and adds, "It is not necessary to lock anything away—you will find that I am completely honest. I am also extremely clean—and not just on the outside either," and she hoists up her black skirt to reveal a snowy white petticoat underneath. "I could also do your laundry," she offers.

"Wonderful! You have a washing machine then?"

"These hands," she cries, raising clenched fists dramatically, "these are my washing machine. The poor cannot afford such luxuries as washing machines, Señora. Also, it is just three months since my mother died and before that things were even more difficult. There were times," she says, her eyes filling with tears, "when there was no money, even for her medicine. Señor Antonio, the one on the fourth floor who used to be a priest, heard of my difficulty and without a word left the money I needed on the table. That man is a saint."

When I pay her the first time, she is overcome with gratitude and plants a kiss on my neck. It makes me uncomfortable to see her so subservient and the second time this occurs I tell her, "Marta, it is not necessary to be so grateful. I am simply paying you the money you have earned."

She seems to accept this, but the third time she charges at me again. Except as she lunges for my neck, I instinctively back off and almost lose my balance while she, having missed her target, pitches forward and almost falls down. We are both embarrassed and after that she accepts her salary more calmly.

One day a letter from New York is lying on the table and Marta asks if she can have the stamps since her son collects them.

"Of course. In the future I will save them for you. How old is your son?"

"He is eighteen—and truly God's blessing—in his first year at the School of Business Administration, and studying very hard." I am surprised that she can afford this.

"He has a scholarship," she explains, "and my daughter helps a little. She is married—and married well—her husband has a trucking company."

"She has children?" Marta's face falls into its saddest contours.

"No, she has none. She, who would be the perfect mother, who loves everything about her home, who is a wonderful cook, who sews, knits, and does exquisite embroidery. For six years she has prayed for a child but it seems hopeless. What a tragedy! Perhaps they will adopt a baby. In any case," she adds, getting back to reality, "my daughter pays for my gas and electricity."

"You have a large apartment?"

"No, Señora, I do not have an apartment. I have a house. A nice little house."

She has never mentioned a husband but one day, as she is dusting, she announces, "Nine years ago, without a word, my husband left. Carlos was nine, my daughter in her teens, and my mother was already an invalid. It has been terribly difficult. I was desperate for money. That was when I started to work for Manuel."

"Your husband doesn't help with Carlos's education?"

"He helps with nothing. We do not even know where he is."

It is the following year and I have been back in Las Palmas almost a month. One day Marta pauses in her cleaning and says in a low conspiratorial voice, "Señora, I am going to tell you a secret. I have told nobody except Don Manuel." A juicy bit of gossip I wonder? "While you were away," she continues, "I came in here one day and that ash tray, which I had left in its usual place on the coffee table, was over there on the kitchen counter." I am not too impressed. "And, in the ash tray," she continues, pausing for effect, "was a *cigarette butt!*" *Now* I am impressed. "It could have been Fernando," she suggests. "He smokes so much he wouldn't even realize he was doing it."

"But how come you told Don Manuel and you didn't tell me?"

"I didn't want to cause trouble."

"Marta, in the future when something occurs here please tell me about it, before you tell Don Manuel or anybody else. Obviously, somebody has a key to the apartment—Fernando, perhaps, or it could be somebody else—and I have been here for a month. You should have told me about it before."

"You are right, Señora. I should have told you. In future I will do so." I pick up the phone.

"Manuel, Marta has just let me into the big secret. Apparently somebody has a key to this apartment and has actually been here while I was away. Could you recommend somebody to change the lock?"

"I, myself, will change it for you," he says, sounding a little sheepish.

"But that is not at all what I intended. I know how busy you are. If you could just suggest a reliable person I should appreciate it very much."

"No, no, it is no trouble. I will do it this very afternoon. After all, one has to be careful about getting outside people to do such things." As promised, he comes and examines the lock. "You need only a new barrel," he explains. "I will go to the hardware store and get one." However, when he returns he finds that the barrel will not fit this particular lock.

"We will have to change the whole thing," he says. "I will go back and get a completely new lock." The hardware store is several blocks away and he doesn't look too pleased. I offer to go and pick it up for him.

"No, no, no," he protests.

"Why not?"

"Because you would not understand what to get," he says impatiently and off he goes. I resent the way he brushed me off and wish now I had called a locksmith.

He returns with the lock and quickly installs it. However, when it comes to putting on the guard designed to protect the lock from burglars, it will not fit.

"So," he says with open disgust, as though he regretted ever having gotten himself into this mess, "this we cannot put on because it is for a door that opens from the right hand side and this door," he says, glaring at it, "opens from the left. Well, it is not really that important," and he puts it aside.

The carton that the lock came in is lying on the kitchen counter and, as I wait for him to gather up his tools, my eye falls on the words—in large letters—FOR DOORS OPENING FROM THE RIGHT.

"If you don't need the old lock," Manuel is saying, "I will put it away. It may come in handy for somebody else."

"No, I don't need it. Perhaps you would like to put it in this carton," and I push it toward him, making sure that the words FOR DOORS OPENING FROM THE RIGHT is facing him. As he reaches for it, his glance flickers briefly, and his lips compress as he stuffs the old lock into it.

"Thank you, Manuel. It was very kind of you to do this and I'm sorry you had to make two trips for the lock. If I were not so stupid about such things I could have gone back for you."

"You are most welcome. It is always a pleasure—and you are not at all stupid," he adds pointedly and disappears.

It is the beginning of another stay in Las Palmas and when I arrive at Casa Manuel, Marta is waiting at the front door.

"I was afraid I would miss you," she says, sounding panic stricken, "and you wouldn't have been able to get in."

"Why not?"

"I had to have new locks put on."

"We had a burglary?"

"No, we did not have a burglary. I threw away the keys. Then I couldn't get in to clean or water the plants, so I had a locksmith open the door and since there were no keys, I had to have new locks put on."

"How did you happen to throw away the keys?"

"Not only the keys, but also six thousand pesetas (about $60)! One day, on my way out, I was carrying my purse and several bags to go into the garbage. At the front door I had so many things I couldn't open it, so I put my purse, just for a second into one of the bags intended for the garbage. But, outside, I met María from next door and we talked for a few minutes. Next morning, I said to Carlos 'where did you put the purse?'—I leave it out so he can take whatever money he needs. 'Mother,' he said 'I didn't see the purse.' Then I remembered. The garbage! I had thrown my purse into the garbage with my money and your keys."

"Marta, that's terrible! I'm sorry you lost your money. But you should have called me about the keys. One of the locks was completely new—the one Don Manuel changed the last time I was here—and there were keys right here in La Palmas. The friends that used my apartment last summer still have a set. Instead you went to the trouble and expense of replacing two locks."

"Well," she says, "that's the Spanish for you. Act first and think later. In any event," she adds, "the expense is of no importance. It was my own fault."

As we exchange news, I notice a change in her. She has lost a good deal of excess weight. Her thick brown hair is shorter and stylishly cut. She is no longer in mourning and she is wearing an attractive print dress. Not only does she seem happier but there are actually stars in her eyes. It occurs to me that perhaps she has met a man who interests her. After all, she is a good-looking woman, not yet fifty, and her life is far from over. I am happy to see the change and delighted that things seem to be taking a turn for the better. Along with the improvement in her appearance has come a new assurance.

"Is this today's paper?" she asks, settling herself comfortably on the couch to scan the headlines. In fact, she is well up on the news and, of the people I know, the only one that even noticed when a letter I wrote about some local problems was published in the newspaper.

"Lenning," she says on anther occasion—as part of the new order she has taken to addressing me by my last name—"Lenning, those flower boxes on the terrace need cleaning out. They are dirty and the few old plants that remain are very ugly. They should be replaced." I don't reply but I know she is right and by the following week there are fresh pots of pink geraniums at both ends of the terrace, all in full bloom. Marta is well satisfied with my efforts.

The week after that, she doesn't show up—which is unusual. A few days later there is a ring at the door. It is Marta. She looks tired and she has been crying.

"Please excuse me for not coming on Wednesday," she says, "but something terrible happened." She is close to tears so I sit her down and fetch a cup of coffee.

"I didn't want to bother you with my problems," she explains, dabbing at her eyes, "so I didn't tell you, but two months ago, just as suddenly as he left, my husband returned—calmly, as though he had gone an hour before, instead of nine years ago—and with no explanation. What could I do? I could not very well turn him away—in any case it is his house. But after all those years during which I had struggled without a word from him, there was no question of reconciliation. Besides, I had learned that he left me for another woman. So he has been staying upstairs and Carlos and I have been living downstairs. After he returned I vowed never to set foot above the first floor.

"Then, last Monday, there was a loud crash overhead and afterwards, silence. I waited. No sound at all. I went up. He was lying on the floor unconscious. I rushed next door for them to call an ambulance and went with him to the hospital. He has had a massive stroke. Now he is in a coma, but thrashing about so that the tubes to which he is connected are in danger of becoming loose. So we are taking it in turns, Carlos, my daughter, and myself, to stay with him. So you see how impossible it was for me to come last week."

"Of course, Marta. Don't worry about it. Is there anything I can do?"

"Thank you, Lenning, but there is nothing anybody can do for the moment."

In spite of her assertion that there has been no reconciliation, it is clear in retrospect that she had been looking forward to just that. Why else the care she had taken to improve her appearance? And those stars in her eyes that I had taken as an interest in some other man, had actually been for her husband with whom she was obviously still in love. Now, with that crash upstairs, all hope of their coming together and making a new life had vanished. I can only try to imagine the heartbreaking disappointment.

"I will be coming back to work next week," she is saying. "After all, life must go on and we need the money more than ever. Perhaps you would explain to Don Manuel. I went to his apartment but he was not there." Later, I go in search of him.

"Marta asked me to explain that she wasn't able to come to work last week because her husband had a stroke. She came to see you but you were out."

"Oh, I am sorry to hear that. In fact, I did not know that he had returned. He is in the hospital?"

"Yes, and in very poor shape apparently. She is extremely upset of course and I feel terribly sorry for her. After all these years—to show up and immediately have a stroke. I wonder if he didn't have some inkling of this beforehand and dumped himself on Marta, knowing that she would take care of him."

"This we cannot say of course."

"No, we cannot say—but we have our suspicions. Not a word or a peseta for nine years—and suddenly, when it's convenient, here he is. It's too unfair. I hope he has the decency to die and get it over." Manuel draws back in consternation.

"Those are very strong words," he admonishes. "One should never wish anybody dead. And, in any case, whatever the circumstances, it is better that he returned."

"Better for whom?"

"Well, obviously better for him but also better for Marta."

"I don't see any great advantage for her."

"Perhaps not in practical or material terms, but in the long run it will be better for her," he replies confidently. "As you probably know, until a few years ago there was no divorce in this country. So husbands who became dissatisfied frequently walked out and set up a new household with somebody else. For the husband this was accepted. But for the wife, living with another man was generally out of the question. So, for her, married life was over. Since, as in Marta's case, many were also left with children to raise, this was a very difficult situation. Now, Marta's husband has added an even greater burden by becoming ill and, naturally, she is very upset. But, whatever the outcome, it is better that he came back. Psychologically it will be to her benefit." A man's point of view, of course. I have my doubts.

And now, each time she comes, she is carrying a large bag filled with fresh linen to take to the hospital after finishing her work. As the weeks go by, I see she is again weighed down with sorrow and many times close to tears. There is a slight improvement in her husband's condition and even signs that he recognizes them, but he still requires constant attention and the routine is beginning to take its toll.

"Why," she exclaims one day, "do such terrible things have to happen to me! What, in God's name have I done to deserve them? Nine years of struggling and just when things seemed to be looking better this has to happen." She is devastated and terrified at the thought of the future, of once again having an invalid to care for. Even her children are upsetting her. "It's Papa this and Papa that," she complains. "Dear Papa! Poor Papa!—as though he had never gone off and left us. And when I remind them of this they say, 'But Mama, he is our *father!*' as though that compensates for everything."

Soon afterwards, I leave for New York and it is four months before I return to Las Palmas. It is a Saturday when I arrive so I don't expect Marta to be here, but she has left fruit and flowers and some basic supplies in the refrigerator. The pink geraniums I planted during my last visit are a mass of blooms and everything is in order. She has obviously taken good care of the place. When I see her on Monday, I immediately ask about her husband.

"Still in the hospital, Lenning," she says hopelessly. "And it's been five months."

"Is he any better?"

"A little. We don't have to stay with him at night any more but I go each day to feed him. He is conscious and seems to recognize us but he can barely speak and he can't see well." Her eyes fill with tears.

"And the rest of the family?" I ask, hastening to get onto a less painful subject.

"All well, thank God, and Carlos about to start his last year at school."

After she has gone, I lament the miserable trick of fate that brought him back—an additional burden for one who already has more than she can cope with. Now, on top of her cleaning jobs and her own household tasks, there are daily visits to the hospital, clothes to be brought home, laundered and carried back, and, above all, the terrible uncertainty about what lies ahead.

And yet, as time passes, I begin to see that not only has she resigned herself to the situation, but that also there is a new confidence that had been completely absent since I had known her—almost a serenity. From a word here and there I begin to understand what her husband's return has meant to her.

"My husband had a fruit and vegetable market," she explains one day, "so he is well known. Now people are always asking 'How is Francisco? Is there any improvement? When will he be coming home?' In a way it is painful but it is also better than before when he was a subject to be avoided. Friends and neighbors not only inquire about him," she adds, "but now that he is back, they speak more freely about their own families, their husbands—matters they had not discussed before in order to spare my feelings. And it is also better for Carlos and my daughter. They were so often embarrassed because people would ask about their father and they were forced to admit that they knew nothing of his whereabouts."

So I begin to understand that whatever problems he has brought, she is no longer an abandoned wife—which is terribly important to her. *Her* husband, unlike most others who leave their wives, has returned. Hers is now a whole family with mother, father—albeit incapacitated—and children. In essence, she has regained her self-respect. I suspect also that she may be better off financially than before. She no longer rushes off to pay the utility bill on the last day before the electricity is to be cut off and every once in awhile she appears in a dress I haven't seen before.

Perhaps, since her husband is in his sixties and has rejoined the family, she is now entitled to social benefits and possibly other compensation because of his illness that she would not otherwise have received. Also, I remind myself, she can now be completely relaxed about the fact that there is no possibility whatever that he will run off with another woman any time soon. So, all in all, although I had lamented his return and wished him a speedy "Adios," it has probably been for the best—just as Manuel had so confidently predicted.

Not in My Bed!

It is the end of August and I am about to leave Las Palmas for New York until after Christmas. In the meantime, Manuel is looking forward to a visit from his daughter and it occurs to me to offer the use of my apartment during her stay. He has been helpful on many occasions when I have needed assistance, so this would be a way to thank him. He is delighted at the suggestion.

"You have solved my problem," he says as I hand over the keys. "I could have slept on the couch and given her the bedroom, but she is bringing another young woman with her and then it would be too crowded."

However, when I return to Las Palmas, Teresa has not yet come.

"She was unable to get away," he explains "but I am expecting her next month," and he returns my keys. That evening the phone rings.

"May I speak to Manuel," says a man's voice.

"I am sorry but this is not his apartment. I will give you his number," and I do. Afterwards, I am puzzled. Where would the caller have gotten my number?

Next day, when Marta comes to clean, I ask her why she has moved the gas cylinder.

"Oh, I never touch it, Señora. I am afraid of gas. Don Manuel must have done it while he was here."

"Don Manuel was here?" Marta looks confused.

"I think he might have been," she says hastily. "Would you like me to wash the windows today?"

Had Manuel stayed in my apartment while I was away? That was not what I had intended. And how come he didn't mention it? That evening there is another phone call for him—a woman this time.

"You have the wrong number," I say curtly and hang up. It seems fairly clear that he was staying here and I am not happy about it. I would like to discuss it with him but I do not want him to think that Marta "told" on him. After all she works primarily for him and it could be awkward for her.

The following morning, fresh from the shower, I pull out the drawer containing my underwear and there at the back, unnoticed when I put the stuff in, is a knitted shirt that I recognize as Manuel's. I don't like the look of it lying there beside my bras and pants. So he was here. In and out of my apartment as though he lives here. Giving people my telephone number as though it were his own. Perhaps entertaining his friends. What a nerve!

As I remove his shirt from the drawer I reflect on his daily routine as he used *my* things, bathed in *my* tub, and worst of all, slept in *my bed!* Suddenly I am furious. Calm down—you are overreacting, I tell myself. But as I look at the bed and picture him curled up in it with his head on my pillow, I am suddenly in such a rage that I have to ask myself—what is this all about? Is it because he has injected himself into my life without my having any say in the matter? Perhaps. Am I upset about the woman who called? It could be.

Next morning he is in the lobby when I leave the elevator.

"A very good morning to you," he says cordially, unaware of the gathering storm. "How are you today?"

"Well, thank you, Manuel. Do you have a moment?"

"Of course." We stand to one side.

"Manuel, we are good friends are we not?"

"We are very good friends," he says smiling as he places a hand on my shoulder.

"Then we can speak frankly to one another?"

"Indeed, we can," and the hand gives a reassuring pat.

"Then, Manuel, I must tell you that I am not comfortable with the idea of your staying in my apartment during my absence." The hand is snatched away as he springs to attention, his face flushed.

"I was there for twelve days," he snaps. "How much do I owe you?"

"You don't owe me a thing. But I offered you the apartment for Teresa. I did not expect that you would be using it for yourself—particularly since she was not even here. I learned of this because I have been receiving phone calls intended for you. Also, you left a shirt behind. Perhaps you would like to come back up with me and collect it."

"Thank you," he says shortly, as I hand it over and he leaves without a word.

"That's done it!" I tell myself. But I am still mad enough not to care and each time I look at the bed I boil over.

"Please launder the bed cover," I instruct Marta. "And have the blankets dry cleaned."

Next day, Manuel is in the elevator when I get on. Indignantly and without fanfare, he says, "I brought my own bedding to your apartment. I did not use *yours.*" Oh, God! Did Marta tell him?

And the day after that, "Even if Teresa had come during your absence, I would not have put them in your apartment. Young girls of that age do not always take good care of things. I, myself, would have stayed there. I had unexpected visitors. It did not occur to me that you would mind."

"Manuel, please don't worry about it anymore," I beg. "It was simply a misunderstanding. I felt we could be frank with one another without getting upset about it. May I invite you for lunch one day this week?"

"Thank you but I am very busy," and he stalks off. Now I realize how deeply offended he is. I still believe I am right but I wish Marta had not tattled to him about my having the bedclothes washed and dry cleaned. I must think of a way to get us back on good terms.

"So, how about our lunch?" I ask the following week. "When would be a convenient day?"

"Perhaps Thursday," he say grudgingly.

Manuel, the soul of punctuality, is late for our appointment and when he appears I see immediately that this is no reconciliation. As I have humiliated him so am I to be humiliated. Besides the familiar yachting cap, he is wearing a pair of well-worn slacks and the knitted shirt he had left in my apartment. He has not shaved and his shoes are unshined. Never before have I seen him look unkempt. I am tempted to back out but decide against it. However, I am ashamed of his appearance and he, although defiant, is obviously ill at ease. Our conversation on the way to the restaurant is forced and there are uncomfortable silences.

At lunch he behaves like a spoiled child trying to show how bad he can be. In fact, for all intents and purposes—apart from the check—I could just as easily not be there. He orders his drink, his lunch, his wine, and without a glance in my direction waves away a basket of bread intended for both of us, then complains that the coffee is cold, and is generally so disagreeable that I am relieved when it is over, and furious with myself for having given him the opportunity to hurt my feelings—which he has.

There have now been several weeks of frigid encounters and I miss our old camaraderie. In spite of the differences which arise from time to time, I reflect, we have a good solid relationship of many years standing. Soon, I will be re- turning to New York and I hate the idea of everything not being right between us before I leave. Then I have an idea. A few days before my departure, aware that I am risking another rebuff, I seek him out.

"Manuel, I wonder if you would mind keeping these while I am away?" and I extend a set of keys to my apartment. He looks surprised and eyes them suspiciously. "In case of emergency," I explain, "or if Marta should lose hers, as she did once before, I would feel much more comfortable knowing that you have a set." He takes them—albeit reluctantly.

It is my way of suggesting that we let bygones by bygones and it seems to help, for there is a noticeable softening in his attitude. This morning, for example, he has come by with my mail, which I interpret as a conciliatory gesture.

"While you are here, Manuel, could I ask your advice about something?" I ask, leading the way into the bedroom. I arrive at the head of the bed and turn to speak to him but he is not there. I look back. Manuel, clearly apprehensive, is toeing what appears to be an imaginary line drawn from one side of the doorway to the other. I regard him curiously.

"I wanted to ask you about a loose connection on the telephone," I explain. His expression clears immediately and he hurries forward eager to examine it.

What did he think? That I was inviting him to bed? If so, his reaction has come as something of a surprise and it occurs to me that I, who have always been careful to maintain a certain distance between us, need not have been so concerned. After all, it takes two to tango, and Manuel seems as shy of the dance floor as I am.

Encounters—An Inside Job

A severe drop in tourism over the past year has led to increased unemployment and a surge in street crime, especially purse snatching. This has caused many of us to take precautionary measures. For example, we no longer carry handbags but stash away anything of value on our person and the rest of the stuff—such as make-up, combs, tissues, personal papers, etc.—goes into a plastic bag heavily disguised as groceries.

I, myself, carry my keys snapped to my underwear and a small purse tucked into my bra. The man at the newspaper kiosk, accustomed to women extracting money from various intimate locations, gazes discreetly into space as I fish for it. It's a good thing to remember that high neck lines can complicate matters. The sort of loose, easily opened attire worn by nursing mothers is ideal.

Now, back at my apartment building, I unclip my keys from their secret place, unlock the front door, enter, and lock it behind me. Since I am now safely inside, I also extract the small purse from my bra. I am at the communal letter box just inside the entrance sorting through the mail when a young man approaches the door, which consists of open bars. I ask him what he wants.

"I am looking for somebody," he says with a smile I do not trust.

"Who are you looking for?" I ask coldly and ungrammatically.

"For that person," he says, pointing to a large envelope which I had placed on top of the letter box.

Like a fool I look up and, as I do, his hand shoots between the bars, snatches the purse out of my hand, and he is off and running.

Whistling in the Dark

Normally I wake up well before daylight and several times lately, as I was lying in bed, the silence has been broken by somebody whistling—but a rather strange series of whistles, definitely not a tune, for example. Then as I paid closer attention, I became aware that, faintly, in the distance, there seemed to be a response. At that hour it sounded eerie and my thoughts turned to such things as smuggling and drug trafficking.

With national boundaries disappearing within the European Community, the Canary Islands, politically part of Spain in spite of their distant location, provide a convenient gateway to Europe for both legal and illegal activities. At such an hour the chances of those activities being legal seemed remote.

There it is again. This time I decide to get up and investigate. It seems to be coming from the area below my apartment where the fishing boats are drawn up. Although the beach is lit all night, there are shadows around the boats that make it difficult to see clearly what is going on. I remember my binoculars and just as I scan the beach the whistling begins again. Now I can see a figure in the shadows with his hands to his mouth. He is obviously the one. I slip on a robe and go out onto the terrace, being careful to keep well back out of the light. Then I hear the answering whistle that I had heard before. It seems to be coming from the hills behind my apartment building. Puzzled and somewhat disturbed, I am still thinking about it later in the day when I encounter Manuel. Not wishing to appear an alarmist, I wait until we have chatted about other matters before I broach the subject.

"By the way," I remark casually, "have you noticed somebody whistling early in the morning from time to time?"

"Not that I recall—but what do you mean by 'early in the morning'?"

"Around 5:30."

"Dios mío! Who is awake at 5:30!" In any event, whistling is hardly exceptional.

"Of course not. But these seem to be people signalling to each other and I have noticed it on several occasions."

"Ah, now you say 'signalling'; I can tell you immediately what it is," he responds with obvious satisfaction at being in a position to instruct me. "Several years ago," he explains, "the daughter of one of the fishermen who lives up the hill married Ortiz Romero, a man from Gomera. They remained on that island for awhile but she missed her family and when her father died they came back here to live with her mother."

I wonder what all this has to do with my question. It's not like Manuel to be so indirect.

"Recently," Manuel continues, "the husband's brother, José, also came here to live. Now, if you have been to Gomera...." I had to admit that I had not. "Ah, then I must explain to you that it is by far the most rugged of the islands—volcanic like the others but with even deeper ravines and sharp, almost insurmountable, ridges. But," Manuel hesitates, "in order for me to answer your question properly, it is necessary to go into some historical background. Perhaps you do not have time for that."

"Yes, of course I do. I should like to hear it." He looks pleased.

"Well then, long before the Spanish conquered these islands in the fifteenth century, they were inhabited by the Guanches, a tall, blond people whose origins have never been clearly established. They were subjected to numerous incursions from various outside groups either wanting to settle here or to capture them and carry them off as slaves. Because of the rough terrain and the difficulty of communicating between settlements, the Guanches warned one another of approaching danger by whistling across the intervening valleys. In Gomera, tests have shown that this type of alert can run through the entire island in half an hour.

"Gradually, over a long period of time, the system of alarms was elaborated as a means of communicating on other matters—and this occurred more particularly in Gomera because, as I have said, it is especially rugged. Eventually, the 'Gomera Whistle', as it is known, became almost a language. It has two vowels and four consonants, plus certain other variations depending upon the pitch—sharp or flat. Actually," Manuel explains, "it is more of a mechanism than a language in the true sense of the word—a system of phonetics that can be used to duplicate a few basic essentials of any language known to the people who wish to communicate with one another.

"So, to get back to your question, what you hear in the morning could be Ortiz whistling to his brother, 'Bring gasoline for the outboard' or 'Don't forget the lunch like you did yesterday'."

"But this is all quite fascinating," I respond.

"Yes, it is very interesting. And it is a real art—unfortunately, an art that is in danger of being lost. With improved communications, particularly the telephone, the Gomera Whistle seems about to disappear. Only some old-timers and the interest of people such as anthropologists have kept it alive. Now, however, there is a movement to have it taught in the schools as part of the island's heritage. It is the kind of thing that children would enjoy, provided of course, they do not realize they are studying history, and it would make them aware that this is a practical means of communication utilized not so long ago—by their grandparents, for example."

"Can you do it?" I ask.

"Me? I can barely whistle for my dog, but I can tell you how they go about it. One doubles a finger under the tip of the tongue, presses the finger with the lips and the teeth and expels air directly from the lungs—not the mouth." He demonstrates but there is no sound.

"So, with respect to José and Ortiz," he adds, "being from Gomera, they probably enjoy speaking to one another in this way. It sets them apart from the others and, undoubtedly, makes them feel quite special. In addition, they have become part of the research project on the subject, which has also raised their status, and perhaps encourages them to practice more than is absolutely necessary."

In the privacy of my apartment, I place a bent finger under my tongue, as Manuel instructed, press the finger with my lips and teeth, fill my lungs to capacity and expel a great burst of air, fully expecting a piercing whistle. Nothing but a silent dribble.

It is obvious that I am not going to become an expert in the Gomera Whistle any time soon. But at least my anxieties have been put to rest and the next time I hear whistling in the pre-dawn hours, I can listen with the satisfaction of an insider who knows what it's all about—even if I don't get the message.

Manuel Sees His Daughter
to the Airport

Downstairs the front door clangs shut and I awake to hear the voices of Teresa and her friend. I look at the clock—5:45. Now I remember. They are leaving today. They must be on their way to the airport. A few minutes later I hear the door being unlocked and somebody rushes in. A few minutes after that the door clangs shut again as somebody rushes out. Then I hear Manuel calling urgently "Taxi! Taxi!"

After a few more minutes I hear Teresa and her friend coming in again. Perhaps they forgot something, I speculate. Then I hear their agitated voices as they go out and the door clangs shut yet again. A car door slams. Then silence and I go back to sleep.

Later in the morning I see Manuel and innocently inquire, "Did Teresa get off okay?" He claps his hand to his forehead in a gesture of extreme suffering.

"This morning," he groans, "was a complete disaster!"

"Really? What happened?"

"As you know, while Teresa was here I have been staying in an apartment in the building around the corner. For this morning, we agreed that I would get a cab and pick up the girls at 5:30 to go to the airport. I was already awake at 4:30 so I got up, showered, shaved, dressed—all in leisurely fashion. Then I turned on the radio and it was not 5:00 A.M. as I thought but 6:00 A.M.

"My ridiculously expensive, extremely complicated watch shows the date, the day of the week, the month, the year, the phase of the moon, your wedding anniversary, your wife's birthday, and who knows what else. It is waterproof, shockproof, gives you the time in the principal capitals of the world, but apparently it is completely unable to provide the correct time here in Las Palmas.

"So I threw on the rest of my clothes and rushed around the block to pick up the girls. They had already gone! I assumed they had left for the airport without me—without even saying goodbye! I couldn't believe it! I rushed out and found a cab, promised the driver a small fortune if we arrived at the airport before the plane left at seven. Clearly, he needed the money because we flew.

"I raced to the check-in counter. No, the plane had not yet left, they informed me. 'I wish to go and say goodbye to my daughter,' I explained. 'It is not possible,' they said. 'The plane is already loaded and it is about to leave.' I argued and, as you can imagine, the whole situation developed into quite a scene—a shouting match in fact. Then, above our raised voices, I heard 'Papa! Papa!' It was Teresa and her friend just arriving at the terminal! They rushed to the counter. 'Are we too late?' asked Teresa. 'No, they were paging you a few minutes ago. I think they will let you board,' she said, scanning the tickets in a big hurry. Then she stopped. 'Ah, you are connecting in Madrid with Flight 304 to London. But that flight has been cancelled because of a strike at Heathrow. You are now scheduled for a flight tomorrow morning which will put you into Gatwick. I will change your tickets,' and she did. Then, as we returned we were able to explain what happened.

"When 5:30 came and I had not appeared, the girls waited for awhile, then became anxious and went out to get a taxi and pick me up. But when they came to my apartment it was already after six and I was not there. I had gone to their apartment, looking for them of course, but they did not know that and when I found them gone, I assumed they were on their way to the airport. So that is when I went racing out to get a taxi. In the meantime, they returned to their apartment but I was not there either, having already left. It was really like one of those old slapstick movies with everybody chasing each other around the block and in and out of apartments, barely missing one another.

"So then they felt compelled to leave but they were behind me, not in front as I supposed. And I continued to get further ahead as I was almost airborne at the time on account of this driver so determined to win the jackpot by getting me to the airport before the plane left.

"What an anticlimax! After the level of excitement connected with our departure and the emotion of parting which, nevertheless, did not take place, we came back quite depressed—except for the driver, who was deliriously happy. I still feel empty at the thought of being without my daughter," he added, pressing his hands to his chest. "It is as though she has already gone.

"So," he continues glumly, "we have to do it all over again tomorrow. But," he adds, brightening, "it should go quite well this time because we are extremely well rehearsed. And, in the meantime, I have unearthed a watch which I bought ten years ago from a street vendor for five dollars, and which still keeps perfect time."

In the News—Sex Anyone?

Sex is frankly discussed and its availability regularly advertised in the morning paper, although at that hour, a "liberated blond"—even one with her own apartment, who accepts Visa and Master Card—may be greeted with a yawn and the fact that "ten exuberant young women who specialize in executives" are waiting for you, may give rise to a shudder. But then there's Antonio, "muy atletico, muchas variaciones." He will come to your home, maximum discretion. One advertisement says "Ménage a trois—English spooken."

In yesterday's paper we had the conclusion of a marital scandal, which for months, has engrossed the whole country. Two sisters, probably the wealthiest women in Spain, were wooed in their youth by two financially-astute cousins, each of whom was named "Alberto." Over the years, "Los Albertos" as they came to be known, maneuvered themselves into powerful positions in the financial world, mainly through the holdings of their wives. However, just as they approached the pinnacle of success, both were discovered to be having extramarital affairs. The sisters immediately divorced them and repossessed their riches.

Yesterday's piece dealt with the collapse of the Albertos' empire. For me, however, the most interesting part was the journalist's final comment. "This," he warned, "is what can happen when one takes the vaginal route to power."

But that was yesterday. Today, the Spanish who derive wicked satisfaction from the fall of persons in high places, are holding their sides over a different kind of amorous disaster.

It seems, the director of a well-known but unnamed bank has been having a discreet affair with his secretary. Discreet, that is, until a "passionate encounter" in his office during which his "member," as the newspaper delicately describes it, became trapped in her intrauterine device. Unable to extricate himself, he was forced to call for assistance and, like a couple of Siamese twins, the two had to be carted off to the hospital to become "disengaged."

A Dream Comes True

Manuel seems discontented lately and he is gaining weight—there is even a slight paunch which would have been inconceivable just a few months ago. Also, during the past weeks, I have encountered some rather unusual young women on their way to and from his apartment—"tarts," I think might be the right word. One in particular I have come to recognize and today, as he and I are returning along the Paseo after lunching together, she is on the beach.

"Hola! Papa!" she calls, waving impudently. Manuel manages a frosty smile and acknowledges her greeting with a dignified touch to his cap, but is unable to hide his chagrin. Not that he isn't frank about himself.

"I am through with sex," he announces as we continue on our way.

"Really," I murmur.

"Yes. I am immunized," he explains. No response seems necessary, although I could mention that recently, I have noticed some of his antibodies flitting about the hallways. Then, after a few thoughtful minutes, he says, "Some of these young girls are extraordinary. All they think about is sex. When they are through with one man they can't wait to have sex with another. And," he adds reflectively, "there is absolutely nothing they will not do."

"Is that so," I respond amiably. There is a long pause before he continues.

"I believe it would be good for me to get away from here. I do not have enough to occupy me. I am accustomed to being busy—too busy most of the time—and to be idle depresses me, makes me feel that my life is over, that I am sitting about waiting to die."

"Manuel, how can you say that! You're in excellent health, knowledgeable, full of ambition—you have a lifetime ahead of you."

"Well, I hope you are right. Of course there is no escaping the fact that, eventually, one has to grow old. But lately I see a good possibility of growing old quite disgracefully. It happens. I see it all the time in men of my age. In some cases it may be an effort to recapture their youth, or to compensate for things they feel they have missed, to indulge themselves before it is too late. In my case it is simply an escape from boredom. I must concentrate more on selling the two commercial floors in 'Casa Manuel'."

"Any prospects?"

"Yes. There are several who are interested—one local businessman in particular. But until now I have not pursued the matter because I thought my daughter might return. Now she has decided to remain in England so I will go ahead and try to dispose of them."

"If you sell them, where would you go?" I ask. Privately, I am dismayed at the prospect of Manuel leaving.

"Perhaps to South America—somewhere with space to keep animals." In general, Manuel's English is very precise, so it does not occur to me that when he says "animals," he actually means "cattle."

"But why do you have to go to South America to keep animals? Why not buy a few acres here in the north—you could keep a couple of dogs, a horse, chickens, maybe even a cow." He looks at me disdainfully.

"That is not what I have in mind."

A few weeks later he manages to close a deal for his commercial space—probably for well over a million dollars—and he is jubilant. Now, since the transfer of pesetas is restricted, and because he would like to get the money out of the country, he is casting about for ways to accomplish this. Very shortly I will be returning to the United States—a fact that has not escaped his attention.

His first suggestion is straightforward—elegantly simple. I should simply walk out of the country with a large bag of his pesetas. I look at him in disbelief.

"Nobody will bother you," he assures me.

"Manuel," I protest, "they put people in jail for that sort of thing!"

"No, no," he purrs, "they wouldn't put you in jail." I am not convinced.

His most recent proposal is more complicated. In essence, it has to do with my using his pesetas to purchase an entire cargo of fish—fishing being a major industry in the Canaries. At the end of some fancy negotiations during which the fish are to change hands several times, I am supposed to end up with large quantities of U.S. dollars. Except I have this uneasy feeling that what I could very easily end up with is a huge quantity of fish.

"Are you serious, Manuel?" I ask incredulously.

"Not really—it was just an idea," he says airily.

Actually, I think he was rather hoping I might rise to the occasion and I sense a feeling of disappointment that I am being unnecessarily cautious and not too cooperative.

In the meantime, the new owner of the commercial floors is stripping everything down to the basic construction elements before rebuilding to suit himself, and Manuel is directing the workmen. Since it was he who built the place, nobody knows better how to take it apart. I catch a glimpse of him from time to time, very dirty and obviously having a good time.

While this is going on, the plumber comes to repair a faucet in my bathroom. This requires that he turn off the water supply to my apartment, but when he attempts to do so he finds that the connection is corroded and needs to be replaced. It is a good time to change it because, at the moment, the water supply to the whole building has been turned off—probably because of the work downstairs.

"I need to go out and buy a new valve," Pepe explains. "In the meantime, perhaps you would ask Don Manuel not to turn on the water until I get back and finish work on this."

I go downstairs where there is banging, crashing, and clouds of dust but no sign of Manuel.

"Is Don Manuel around?" I ask one of the workmen. He nods and points to a ladder. At the top I see what I assume is the lower half of Manuel. The rest is poked up through a jagged hole in the ceiling.

"Manuel!" I call, trying to shout above the din. He doesn't hear. Then the workman bellows for me, "Don Manuel!" The feet descend a couple of rungs and he ducks his head out. His face is grimy and sweaty and he does not look pleased to see me.

"Si?" he demands impatiently.

"It's about the water," I shout. His face flushes, his lips compress in anger, and he glares at me.

"The water! The water!" he screams throwing up his hands in exasperation. "The water will be turned on as soon as I have finished what has to be done!" I am astonished at his rudeness.

"But, Manuel," I try to interject. He pays no attention and continues to shout.

"We are not playing games here, Señora!" *Señora*, no less! "We do not turn the water off for fun. I am working as fast as I can so that we can have water as soon as possible. If I could just work without interruption it would be even sooner!"

"And if you would just *listen* to me," I retort angrily, "it would be even sooner than *that*. I came to ask you *not*, repeat *not*, to turn the water on!"

Manuel freezes, drops his hands helplessly to his side, and stares straight ahead as though confronting some inevitable disaster.

"The plumber is working in my apartment," I add and make for the exit. When I go back upstairs, Pepe has returned and is at work. Soon after, Manuel appears. I am still fuming and wonder if he will apologize, but he just stands behind Pepe watching him. Pepe is a quiet, capable man who doesn't take kindly to interference, so he ignores Manuel. I have no intention of ever speaking to him again during my entire lifetime, so I have nothing to say. Finally Manuel breaks the silence.

"Pepe," he says quietly, "please let me know when you have finished. I will be downstairs."

"Very well. It will be just a few more minutes."

So there is to be no apology. I cannot let this pass. Manuel goes out to the elevator and I follow. He pulls open the door and gets in. Before the door can close I have my hand on it and hold it open.

"Manuel," I say, as quietly and sweetly as I can, "has it *occurred* to you that you may be working too *hard*? That perhaps you are becoming so nervous and excited that your *temper* may be getting out of hand?" He stares past and beyond me, expressionless.

"Please close the door."

The following day on my way out, he stops me in the lobby.

"It is not that I am working too hard or getting too excited," he says, apropos of nothing. "It is just that *six people* had already interrupted me to ask 'When is the water going to be turned on?', 'When is the water going to be turned on?'. I was already having difficulty and there is a limit to my patience."

"I was not asking you 'When is the water going to be turned on?'," I remind him icily.

"But you said 'It's about the water.' How could I know?"

"In other words, it was *my* fault."

"Not at all. I am only *trying* to *explain*," he insists, his voice rising.

"I see. You will have to excuse me, Manuel, I am late for an appointment," and I leave. I maintain the chill for almost a week but, as in the past when one or the other has nursed a grievance, there is a gradual thaw and eventually we are back on our old footing—whatever that is. Manuel has not apologized of course—he never does. On the other hand, I tell myself, his "explanation" *could* be considered a sign of remorse. When I return for my next visit to Las Palmas, Manuel is away exploring Argentina.

"I have bought a ranch!" he cries exuberantly at our first encounter following his return.

"How wonderful!" I exclaim, trying to match his enthusiasm although I do not think it is at all wonderful. "Tell me about it."

"It is located on a broad plain at the foot of the Andes—dry and with very little vegetation, for there is hardly any rain in that area. However, there is a good supply of underground water. All one has to do is pump it up and irrigate. The land is very fertile—I saw wonderful crops of alfalfa grown with this system."

For the next few weeks, Manuel is racing in all directions. In addition to arrangements for packing and shipping his personal belongings, he has to sell his apartment. However, he thrives on activity and is clearly excited about his latest adventure. For so long, to have a ranch has been his dream and now it is about to come true. Once more he has a purpose in life.

It is now just a few days before his departure and the owners of the apartments in the building have organized a farewell dinner for him at the new restaurant downstairs.

As I approach the space reserved for our group, a well-tailored, bald-headed gentleman murmurs, "Very elegant, Señora!" One is always pleased by a compliment but, from a stranger, it is a surprise. Then I look again.

"Manuel!" I gasp, "I didn't recognize you! You look—magnificent!"

"Well, I thought I should show my appreciation by dressing appropriately for this occasion," he responds, smiling and bowing slightly. It is not only his attire that makes the difference, however. Without the ever-present cap that has disguised his loss of hair, he looks completely different.

The dinner is a jolly affair and Manuel is obviously touched by the fact that virtually every person in the building has come.

"You did not realize that you were so well loved," I say from the other side of the table.

"No, I did not and I am troubled. A little more of this and it is possible that I will change my mind about leaving," he responds—but he does not of course.

The day before he is to leave, he comes to say goodbye.

"Manuel, you must give me your address," I say as I pour our drinks.

"In fact, at this moment I do not have an address. The house on the ranch was unoccupied for some time and it has been vandalized—it lacks doors and windows, for example. But a few miles from my property is a small village so, while I was negotiating for the ranch, I lived there in a boarding house and became friends with the owner—and his daughter. She is already in love with me of course. I will continue to stay there until my house is made habitable so I will give you that address."

The thought of Manuel out there in the wilderness alone—or almost alone—makes me uneasy. Suppose he becomes ill—maybe has another heart attack?

"How far is the closest large city?" I ask diplomatically.

"About 150 miles."

"Is your ranch very big?"

"Fifteen hundred acres—just what I was looking for."

"And what will you do with it?"

"I will keep animals. The present owner has 250 cows which he will sell to me at a good price."

"Then you are going to have a dairy farm?" I ask in surprise.

"Dairy farm?" he says uncertainly.

"A farm that sells milk and cream."

"Of course I am not going to have a dairy farm," he says contemptuously.

"Then what are you going to do with 250 cows?"

"They will be fattened and sold for meat."

"Isn't that rather unusual?"

"I see you know nothing about farming."

"Manuel!" I protest indignantly. "I was born on a farm and I know enough that if you intend to raise beef you don't buy a bunch of cows. You buy steers."

"Steers? What are steers?"

"Steers are castrated bulls."

"Ah!"—with an expression of enlightenment—"Yes, that is what he has. Excuse me, I made a mistake. It is—what is the word?—'steers' that he has." Manuel, who prides himself on his correct use of English is obviously annoyed at having blundered. "So, as usual, you know more than I gave you credit for," he adds.

"Not at all. As you are well aware, your English is excellent, but for you this is a new vocabulary. And, by the way, 'cow' is 'vaca' in Spanish, which is why I was surprised that you were buying 250 of them to fatten up for beef."

"Ah, Diós mio—how stupid I am! I suppose it is quite appropriate," he says after a moment's reflection, "that we should be arguing even as we are about to part—perhaps for the last time. But that is natural, of course, for we are frequently at cross purposes."

"Not really Manuel. On important matters I believe we understand one another very well."

"Perhaps too well."

"What do you mean?"

"Over the years, I have come to understand that you are very much afraid of being dominated. This makes you cautious, especially in your dealings with men. Too cautious, perhaps, to marry again—or even to have a lover. I also believe there are times when you wish this were not so." I am caught unawares.

"Is this so apparent?"

"Not at all. I know it because it is a reflection of myself. And, as you probably realize, this has been the cause of many of our conflicts."

"But our conflicts have not been important."

"Of course not—on the contrary, they have served to make things more interesting—but this is because both of us have been careful to keep a good distance between us."

"I shall miss you, Manuel."

"But most of the time you were not even here."

"I know, but I liked the idea that you would be here when I returned."

"And I looked forward to your coming," he admits raising his eyes to meet mine. "Things might have been different," he adds, turning away, "if, in the beginning, I had not been married. Of course my wife and I were separated but in those days there was no divorce in Spain. Then, Valentina died and I was a widower. In the meantime, however, you had married and by the time you divorced, I believe we had both reached the point where we no longer trusted ourselves with another close relationship. Even though," he muses, "I must remind you that we have spent some time in the same bed—sequentially of course—and with an ocean between us."

"That was one of our worst crises, wasn't it?"

"Yes. It was almost the end of everything."

"Perhaps it was not such a bad thing, Manuel, that one of us was always 'tethered,' so to speak. It may have kept us from ruining a wonderful friendship. After two husbands and a certain number of lovers, I have come to understand that, for me, friends are the most precious and lasting of all."

"I think you are absolutely right. On this we are in complete agreement. You will always be very special to me. And now, if you will excuse me, I must go and finish my packing. Tomorrow I have an early flight. You, also, will be leaving in a few days. I wish you a safe journey and good luck," and we shook hands.

How I shall miss him! I wish things could have been different and apparently Manuel feels the same way. Suddenly I feel very alone and close to tears. I am glad our parting is over. Then I see his glasses on the table. So it isn't over yet. I call him.

"Manuel, you forgot your glasses."

"Ah, so that's where they are. I will come immediately," and he does.

"I cleaned them," I say, handing them to him.

"Thank you," he replies, awkward and at a loss for a moment. Then abruptly. "How did you know they were dirty?"

"I looked through them and I could hardly see."

"I am very careless about that. Thank you. So goodbye again. By the way," he adds, pausing, "I sold my apartment for twelve million pesetas—around $100,000, U.S. You should ask no less than fourteen million for yours." The door closes and he is gone.